The Lean 6 Sigma Deployment Memory Jogger™

2nd Edition

2 Improve the Process

Publication

The Lean 6 Sigma Deployment Memory Jogger™ 2nd Edition

Development Team

Author: Jaime Villafuerte

Project Manager: Daniel Griffiths

Designer: Janet MacCausland

Publication Review Team

Elizabeth Keim, *Integrated Quality Resources*, LLC

Carolina Jimenez, *Operational Excellence Manager, Bausch & Lomb*

Matt Mercer, *Director of Transformational Lean, Stanley Black & Decker*

GOAL/QPC
8E Industrial Way, Suite 3, Salem, NH 03079
Toll free: 800.643.4316 or 603.893.1944
service@goalqpc.com
MemoryJogger.org

Printed in the United States of America
ISBN: 978-1-57681-150-4

10 9 8 7 6 5 4

REV FH 4.8.13

A Complete How-To Pocket Guide:

Continuous
Improvement
and
Standardization

anagers,
idual, and
rovement
Teams

ustomer/Supplier
Senior Executive
Teams

Stati
Meth
Seven Q
Control
Too

Customer
Driven
Master
Plan

7 Management
and Planning
(7MP) Tools

Information
Systems/Audit
Tools

Quality Systems
Quality Function
Deployment (QFD)

Daily Managem

Planning

Cross-Functional
Management

HORIZONTAL INTEGRATION

HOW

WHAT

WHO

How to Use This Pocket Guide

This pocket guide is designed for you to use as a convenient and quick reference guide. The "*What is it?*" "*Why use it?*" and "*How do I do it?*" format offers you an easy way to navigate through the information in each section. Put your finger on any individual tool within seconds! Use this guide as a reference on the job, or during and after your training, or as part of a self-study program, or to reacquaint yourself with the different types of tools and their uses.

issues, and discovering causes of persistent problems. Deliver bottom-line results or solutions to problems, and assist in personnel selection, performance analysis, conflict resolution, and strategic planning.

Make it Your Own

Take any Memory Jogger and apply your company's own personal style. Customization allows you to creatively combine the contents of GOAL/QPC products with your own documents and training materials. We can deliver to digital eBook or print version.

Know the Tool You Need?

Find it by using the:

Table of contents. Tools, techniques, the case study—it's in alphabetical order.

Solid tab. Look for the blue or black solid box at the bottom of the first page of each new section.

Use this Pocket Guide as a:

- **Quick reference guide:** Quickly identify key points while working on a project or kaizen.
- **Kaizen learning tool:** Use during kaizen events to reinforce the key points.
- **Problem-solving workbook:** Follow the step-by-step process of the Plan-Do-Check-Act Cycle.
- **Way to identify waste and generate kaizen ideas:** Provide the guidelines to "see" waste at your workplace and learn how to eliminate it.

- **Self-paced preparation guide:** A learning guide for the SME, AME, Shingo Prize & ASQ Lean Bronze, Silver and Gold Certification.

To access a PDF version of the forms in this book, visit **MemoryJogger.org/LSS** for downloadable forms.

HELPFUL ICONS

Important or critical information to remember

Additional sources to expand a topic

A reflection point or question to better understand a topic

DO YOU REALLY KNOW L6σ?

QUIZ

1. Visual management aims to:
   a) Make waste visible so you can eliminate it and prevent it from recurring in the future
   b) Make normal and abnormal conditions visible so standards can easily be followed by all employees
   c) Improve our efficiency by effectively communicating
   d) All of the above

2. To recognize waste you start by examining any process from:
   a) The customer's perspective
   b) The manager's perspective
   c) The cost benefits
   d) Staffing considerations

3. Material or work at hand (other than what's needed right now) to satisfy customer demand is an example of which type of waste:
   a) Inventory
   b) Motion
   c) Transportation
   d) Skills unused

4. Searching for materials or parts, reaching for tools, lifting, arranging, and turning on the manufacturing floor is an example of what type of waste:
   a) Motion
   b) Transportation
   c) Overproduction
   d) Inventory

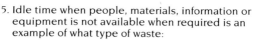

5. Idle time when people, materials, information or equipment is not available when required is an example of what type of waste:
   a) Waiting
   b) Inventory
   c) Transportation
   d) Defects

6. Which tool(s) should be used to identify issues contributing to a problem?
   a) 5 Whys
   b) Fishbone diagrams
   c) Pareto chart
   d) Both (a) and (b)

7. How many times you may ask "why" when looking for the root cause?
   a) A minimum of five times
   b) As many times as necessary to identify the root cause
   c) Five times per hour
   d) Five times

8. Which of the following is a problem solving tool?
   a) Takt time
   b) Kanban
   c) Pareto
   d) 5S

9. What is the goal of Lean Six Sigma?
   a) Remove all waste
   b) Remove all variation
   c) Remove all overburden
   d) All the above

10. What is the pareto principle?
    a) 80% of the problems are not important
    b) 50% of the problems come from 50% of the causes
    c) 80% of the problems come from 20% of the causes
    d) 20% of the problems are not important

11. Which of the following is a Lean Six Sigma guiding principle?
    a) Make problems visible
    b) Mistake-proofing
    c) Plan-Do-Check-Act
    d) Both (a) and (b)

12. Which question should you ask at the check step of the PDCA cycle?
    a) Which obstacles are you addressing?
    b) What did you learn about reaching the target?
    c) What is working?
    d) What obstacles are preventing you from reaching the target?

13. Value stream mapping looks at:
    a) Material and information flow
    b) People and equipment flow
    c) The detail work at each process step
    d) Both (a) and (b)

14. Standard work is the description of the best practice performed by people and machines.
    a) True
    b) False

See last page for answers.

INTRODUCTION

Dear Lean Six Sigma practitioner:

The GOAL **of any Lean Six Sigma deployment** is that everyone becomes a capable agent who contributes to improve Cost, Quality and Delivery every day. The question is then *How can you develop capable people*?

A common approach is to provide individual mentoring in which a sensei, coach, or mentor works with one or a few employees. This alternative requires a patient organization as only a small number of employees are reached at a time and bottom line improvements may take longer than expected.

A better option to develop capable people is to provide a "blended" approach in which mentoring is complemented with "learning by doing" training resources such as this Memory Jogger. This way, everyone in your organization can use *The Lean Six Sigma Deployment Memory Jogger*™ on their own time and at their own pace.

This Memory Jogger provides you with the essential whats, whys and hows following the five deployment steps of lean thinking as presented by James Womack in his breakthrough book *Lean Thinking*.

While implementing *kaizen* and working towards *gemba*, having this pocket guide handy will keep you on track.

— Jaime Villafuerte, ASQ *Master Black Belt*, *Master Lean*

Table of Contents

LSσ Introduction

What is Lean Six Sigma (LSσ)?

LSσ is a management system that includes **tools, methodologies,** and **principles** that focus on providing value to our customers by removing all waste, overburden and variation from our processes.

It must be practiced EVERY DAY BY EVERYONE IN A VERY CONSISTENT MANNER – not in spurts – in a concrete way on the shop floor and in the office.

Visible Results ↑	**Value to our Customers** Quality-Cost-Delivery **Ch 1**		
Tools ↑	**Problem Solving** (e.g., Pareto) **Ch 2**		**Countermeasures** (e.g., 5S) **Chs 4-7**
Methodologies ↑	**Alignment** Policy Deployment Value Stream-Mapping **Ch 4**	**Deployment** Kaizen Events Projects "Just-do-its" **Ch 1**	**Improving** PDCA DMAIC **Ch 2**
Principles	**The Way of Lean Thinking** **Ch 1**		

WHY IS L6σ NECESSARY?

Lean Six Sigma prepares you to provide more value to your customers and face changes with a new way of thinking, and simple but effective problem-solving tools.

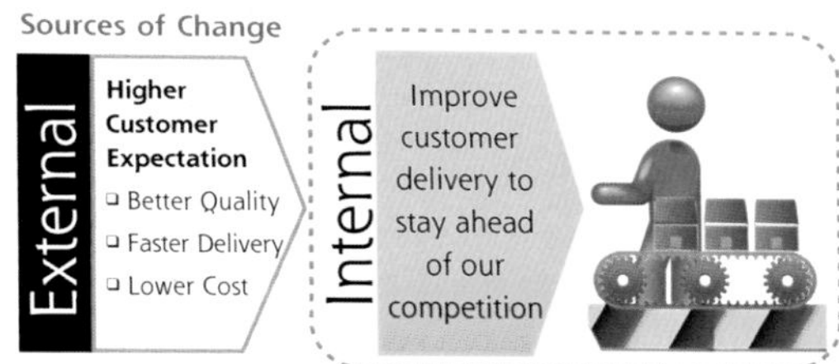

HOW TO OVERCOME RESISTANCE TO CHANGE

As you deploy Lean Six Sigma you will find:

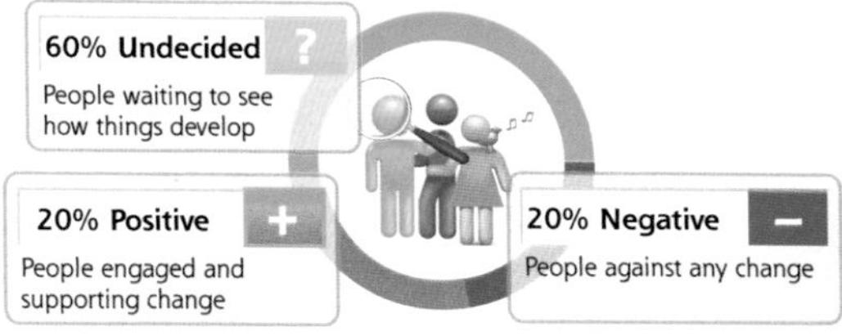

Focus on the **undecided 60%** group that can be influenced through further communication, involvement and support. To focus on the **negative 20%** usually is a waste of time and resources as they will likely reject any change. Leverage the **positive 20%** group but avoid spending more resources or time than required.

By applying the 20-60-20 rule you can leverage the positive 20% while working on the undecided 60%. **A common mistake is to focus on the negative 20%.**

Key Points to Overcome Resistance to Change

- **Communicate:** regular communication about the need for change and the change process itself. Use personal meetings and mass communication means such as email, newsletters or intranet sites to share knowledge and success

If you think you have communicated enough, do it again. There is no such thing as over-communicating in L6σ deployment.

- **Involve:** make people part of the change and seek advice

- **Listen:** create opportunities for people to provide feedback. Personally meet your supporters and detractors. Use the 20-60-20 rule

- **Recognize:** ensure reward and recognition are used for team and individual contributions

We are called to make a conscious decision to accept changes and take action to survive and thrive. As Deming once said, **"It is not necessary to change. Survival is not mandatory."**

What are the Guiding Principles?

They are the fundamental key beliefs, behaviors and reasoning in L6σ.

12 LEAN GUIDING PRINCIPLES

Results	1> Create value for our customers
Velocity	2> Produce only what is needed, when it's needed, in the right amount 3> Eliminate anything that stops the flow of creation
Built-in Quality	4> Never pass a defect onto the next process 5> Build quality instead of inspecting it
Continuous Improvement	6> Relentlessly eliminate waste 7> Embrace scientific problem solving 8> Observe problems first-hand 9> Make problems visible
Cultural Enablers	10> Develop people 11> Promote teamwork 12> Lead with humility

The 12 L6σ **Principles** are built by the deliverable practice and repetition by everyone in the organization. Begin these principles at the top management level and cascade down throughout the organization.

What guiding principles are consistently ignored in the organization and what is the effect on deploying Lean Six Sigma?

WHAT ARE THE LSσ METHODOLOGIES?

By the application of the 12 principles, three methods are required within Lean Six Sigma: **Alignment, Deployment, and Improvement.**

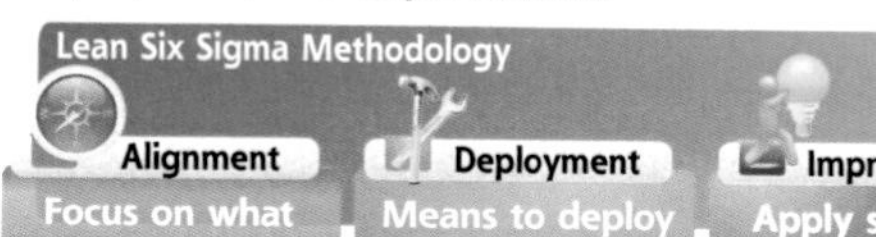

Alignment	Deployment	Improvement
Focus on what really matters	Means to deploy improvements	Apply scientific problem solving
What is important for our organiztion?	How do we deploy improvements?	How do we solve problems?
USE: - Policy Deployment or Hoshin Kanri - Value stream deployment plans	USE: - Kaizen events - Projects - "Just-do-it"	USE: - PDCA - DMAIC *for complex problems*

What are the Alignment Methodologies?

They are the management systems and tools created to align deployment with the LSσ principles and direction. They transform individual efforts into collective actions focused on what really matters to the organization.

See *The Hoshin Kanri Memory Jogger™* for more information.

What are the Improvement Methodologies?

They are the structured approaches to solve problems. The two most common are Plan-Do-Check-Act (PDCA), and *Define-Measure-Analyze-Improve-Control* (DMAIC), but there are many others such as 8 Disciplines or 8D.

In L6σ, the PDCA is used to solve problems, small or big. However, when problems are extremely complex and higher-level statistical analysis and modeling is required, DMAIC is recommended.

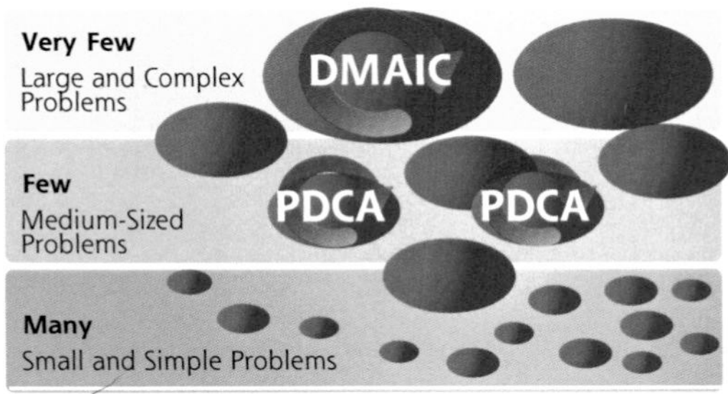

DMAIC is a six sigma approach. Find in-depth study in *The Black Belt Memory Jogger™*.

PDCA and DMAIC methodologies are based on the principle "embrace scientific problem solving" and applicable in office and manufacturing settings. Apply DMAIC when the problem is complex and statistical analysis is required, otherwise PDCA should be enough.

What are the Deployment Methodologies?

They are the different ways to deploy L6σ. The most common are: **kaizen events**, **projects** and **"just-do-it"** or simple kaizen.

1. **Kaizen events** are temporary, intensive, time compressed, 2–5 days, and very disruptive efforts

as several and/or major changes are implemented at the same time. A kaizen event brings together a small but important group of people to improve current processes and fix problems very quickly.

Typical week-long kaizen events:

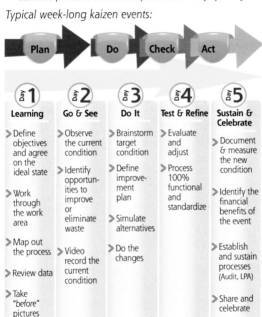

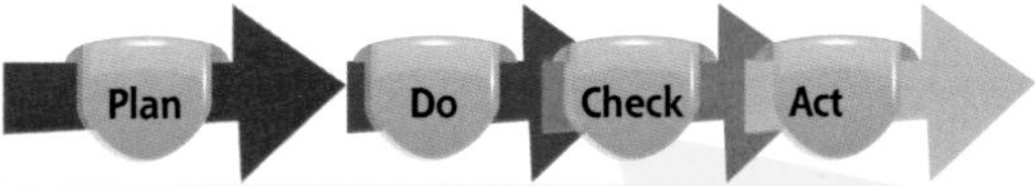

Plan → Do → Check → Act

Day 1 Learning	Day 2 Go & See	Day 3 Do It	Day 4 Test & Refine	Day 5 Sustain & Celebrate
> Define objectives and agree on the ideal state > Work through the work area > Map out the process > Review data > Take *"before"* pictures	> Observe the current condition > Identify opportunities to improve or eliminate waste > Video record the current condition	> Brainstorm target condition > Define improvement plan > Simulate alternatives > Do the changes	> Evaluate and adjust > Process 100% functional and standardize	> Document & measure the new condition > Identify the financial benefits of the event > Establish and sustain processes (Audit, LPA) > Share and celebrate

Learning by doing. Kaizen events are the best way to apply and teach the lean principles while providing meaningful results of at least 50%.

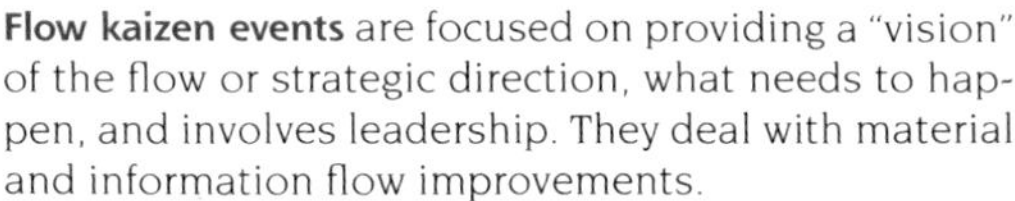

Flow kaizen events are focused on providing a "vision" of the flow or strategic direction, what needs to happen, and involves leadership. They deal with material and information flow improvements.

Process kaizen events are tactical, focusing on how to execute the strategy, utilizing the people closest to the work.

Strategic ↑ — Tactical ↓

Type	Purpose	Who?	Time
Flow Kaizen	Provide a vision of the flow **Value-Stream Improvement**	Leadership	2–5 days
Process Kaizen	People and process flow **Elimination of waste**	Leadership & Employees	2–5 days
Simple Kaizen	Everyday Improvements **Elimination of waste**	Employees	Hours

2. **"Just do it" or simple kaizen** are the everyday improvements done by everyone, individually or in teams lasting hours instead of days.

3. **Projects** are also temporary efforts but less intensive within a longer timeframe, weeks to months, and generally involving complex situations in which DMAIC is the preferred methodology.

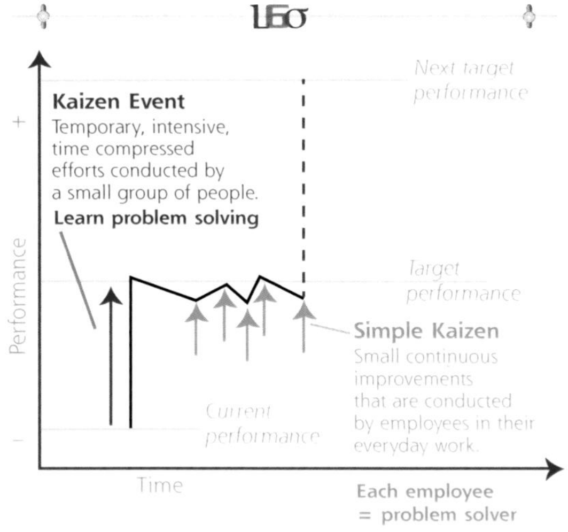
Kaizen Event
Temporary, intensive, time compressed efforts conducted by a small group of people.
Learn problem solving
Next target performance
Target performance
Simple Kaizen
Small continuous improvements that are conducted by employees in their everyday work.
Current performance
Performance
+
–
Time
Each employee = problem solver

Why is simple kaizen critical for sustainability?

A major failure of most LSσ deployment efforts is that gains achieved as a result of a kaizen event are not sustained. It is common to see performance going back to previous low levels if there is not a daily system that prevents slipping back to the "old ways."

This daily system allows adherence to the new target performance by making visual any deviation and then immediately applying **simple kaizen** to improve processes and standards.

Simple kaizen efforts that follow a kaizen event deal with the causes that prevent employees from sustaining the gains obtained during the event.

Model or Learning Line

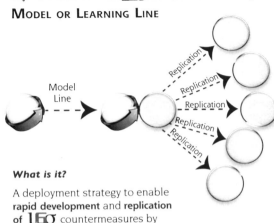

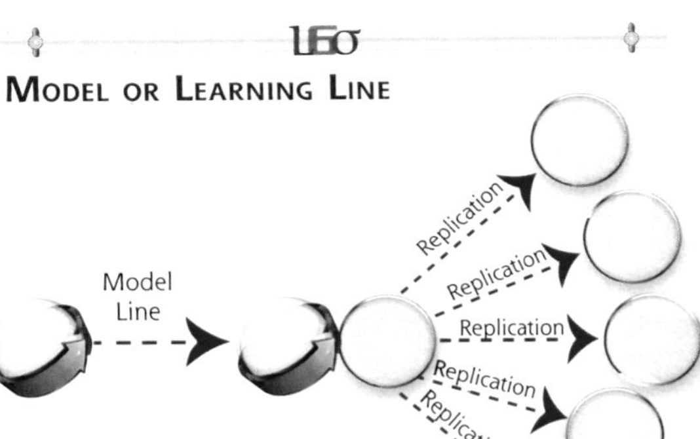

What is it?

A deployment strategy to enable **rapid development** and **replication of L6σ** countermeasures by introducing them first in an area or production line as a model or pilot.

Why use it?

- **To try solutions on the model line** before implementing across the organization
- It is a **showcase of success**, a scale model of the "future state"
- It is **a method to create a pull for replication** that makes it easier to benchmark and replicate

Model Line is a "go and see" what Lean can do for us. Apply the 20-60-20 rule to decide where to start. Look for supporters who are eager to learn by doing.

What are the LSS Tools?

The LSS tools can be identified in two categories: **problem solving** and **countermeasures.**

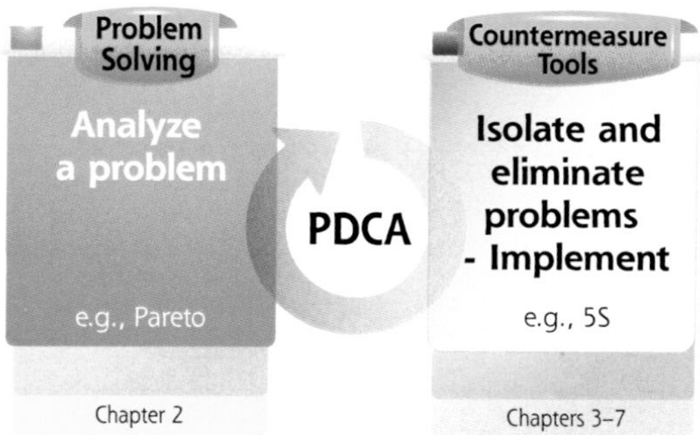

1. **Problem-solving tools:** Use them to help you *analyze* a problem. They are described in chapter two.
2. **Countermeasure tools:** They help *isolate and eliminate problems* as a result of applying the guiding principles. They can be permanent or temporary. Countermeasure tools are covered in chapters three through seven.

Why countermeasures rather than a solution? To prevent static thinking in which changes are permanent solutions. Countermeasures are changes that require you to continuously think about better methods and better countermeasures.

What is the Goal of L6σ?

remove all waste, overburden and variation from processes so only value is provided to customers. **Aim to:**

Improve Safety

Improve Quality

Reduce Response Time

Eliminate Waste

Protect our employees

Protect our customers

Protect our business

To achieve these objectives, L6σ focuses on ***applying principles instead of just pursuing results*** no matter what. L6σ deployment should develop effective and consistent behaviors at all levels of the organization. This will help to drive process optimization and sustain it. Principles drive systems which incorporate tools. Here is an example:

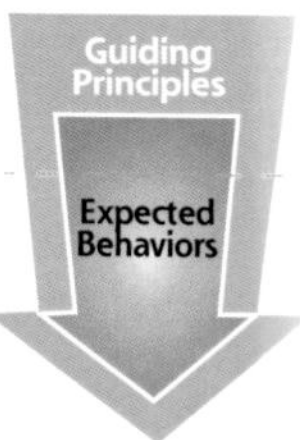

Lead with Humility

- Managers **ask** questions and **seek** input from others
- Managers continuously **work** with others to align systems with ideal behaviors
- Employees actively **learn** new skills from others and **share** their learnings

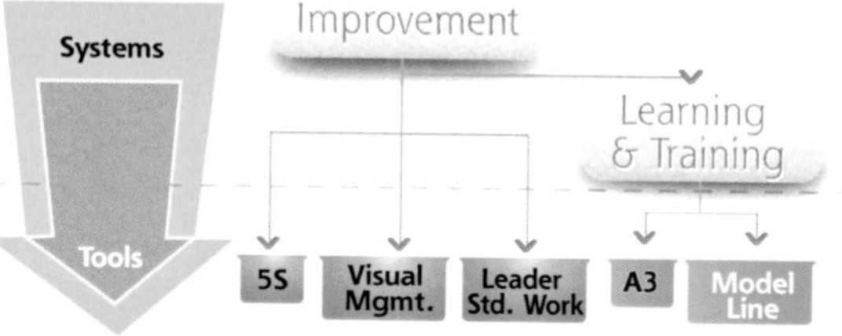

In this example, the *lead with humility* principle drives behaviors such as *Managers ask questions*. To support these behaviors, Improvement Systems are created in which a variety of tools such as 5S and Visual Management are used.

"The only constant in life is change."
— *Heraclitus - Greek Philosopher*

See *The Lean Enterprise Memory Jogger*™ for more information about Visual Management.

How do you Improve?

By following five steps:

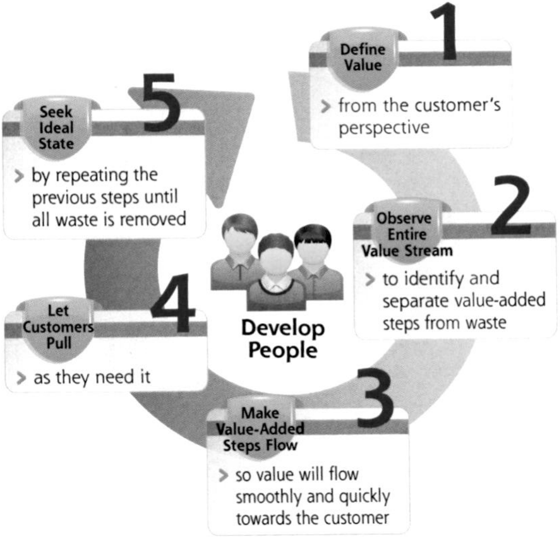

1 Define Value
> from the customer's perspective

2 Observe Entire Value Stream
> to identify and separate value-added steps from waste

3 Make Value-Added Steps Flow
> so value will flow smoothly and quickly towards the customer

4 Let Customers Pull
> as they need it

5 Seek Ideal State
> by repeating the previous steps until all waste is removed

Develop People

Several tools are used in each of these steps as shown in the next diagram, however, each tool should be used only after understanding the 12 Guiding Principles.

Customers want solutions to their problems: the first question is always **"What is the problem that you want to solve?"**

LSσ Tools

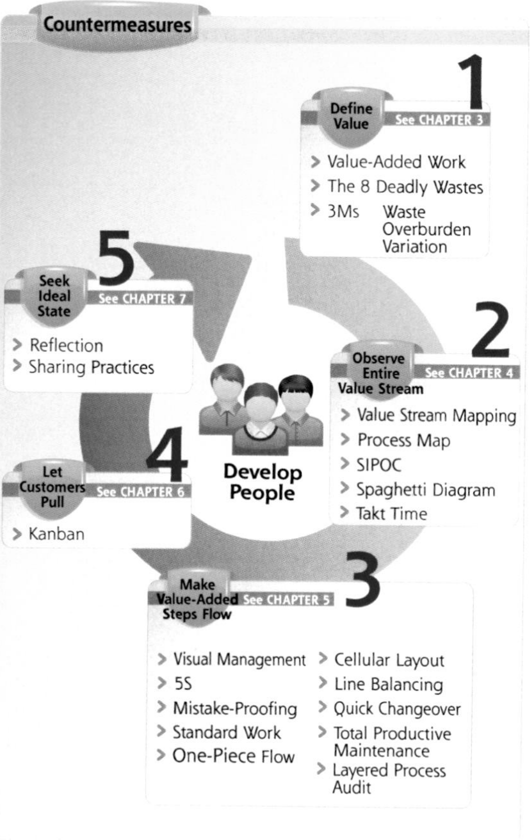

Countermeasures

1 Define Value See CHAPTER 3

- Value-Added Work
- The 8 Deadly Wastes
- 3Ms Waste
  Overburden
  Variation

2 Observe Entire Value Stream See CHAPTER 4

- Value Stream Mapping
- Process Map
- SIPOC
- Spaghetti Diagram
- Takt Time

3 Make Value-Added Steps Flow See CHAPTER 5

- Visual Management
- 5S
- Mistake-Proofing
- Standard Work
- One-Piece Flow
- Cellular Layout
- Line Balancing
- Quick Changeover
- Total Productive Maintenance
- Layered Process Audit

4 Let Customers Pull See CHAPTER 6

- Kanban

5 Seek Ideal State See CHAPTER 7

- Reflection
- Sharing Practices

Develop People

Putting it all Together

Process: *Use the five steps*: (1) Define value, (2) Observe entire value stream, (3) Make value-added steps flow, (4) Let customers pull, and (5) Seek ideal state to eliminate waste, variation and overburden. These five steps are the core of L6σ deployment. At each iteration of the five steps, processes become leaner to provide more value to your customers, and there is better quality, less cost and faster delivery. The faster and more effective each iteration, the faster your L6σ transformation.

People: Make people in your organization responsible to transform their own processes using the five steps. Use the *Guiding Principles* to drive the expected behaviors at each level of your organization. L6σ transformation is not only the job of improvement specialists such as Black Belts but of everyone in your organization. The more capable and engaged your people, the more effective your L6σ deployment.

Problem solving: At each iteration of the five steps, people identify problems and opportunities for improvement. Use *Plan-Do-Check-Act* or *Define-Measure-Analyze-Improve-Control* to solve these problems. Problem-solving tools such as Pareto Chart and countermeasures such as 5S can be used depending on the problem at hand.

Purpose: Define your organization's purpose and make it explicit to everyone so you can align their efforts to solve the problems that really matter the most. Effective and successful L6σ deployment requires a strong alignment of efforts. Use policy deployment or Hoshin Kanri.

Problem Solving

Chapter TWO

Problem Solving

CHAPTER 2

- Problem Definition
- PDCA
- A3 Report
- Practical Problem Solving
- Pareto
- Fishbone
- 5 Whys
- Higher Why

Plan

Plan what you want to accomplish and what you need to get there

Do

Do what you planned on doing

Check

Check the results of what you did to see if the objective was achieved

Act

Act on the information to standardize or to plan further improvements

GO & SEE: We must go & see what really happens in our workplace

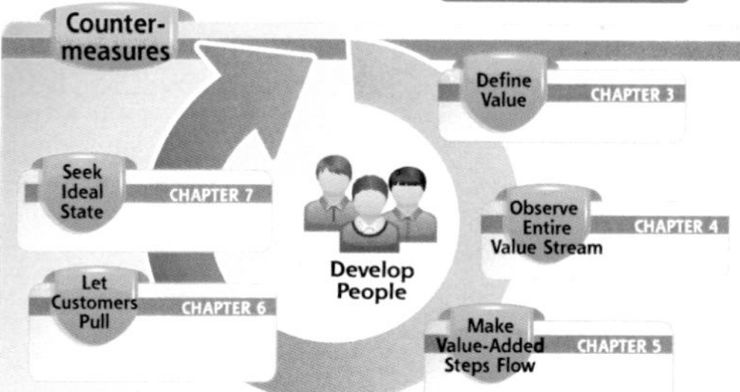

What is a problem?

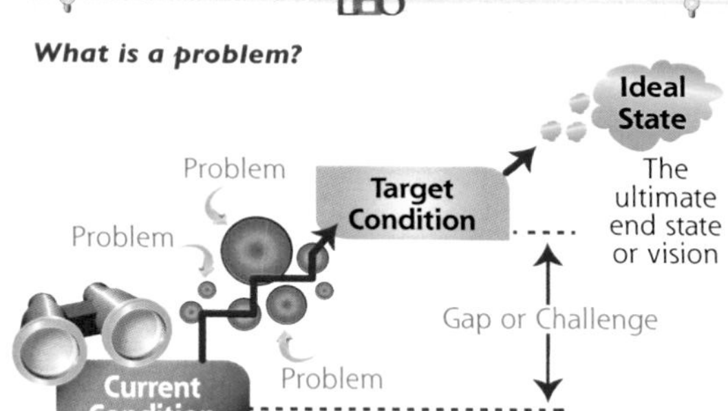

A problem is **anything that prevents you from reaching what you aim to achieve** (your vision). That difference between current and target is the gap or challenge.

Solving problems is continuously removing obstacles, small or big, one by one as you get closer to your target condition.

How do you solve problems?

Use the **Plan-Do-Check-Act (PDCA)** approach to solve problems, small or big. In some cases, when problems are extremely complex, you may need to use the **Define-Measure-Analyze-Improve-Control (DMAIC)** approach, which is a six sigma problem-solving methodology.

Having a vision (ideal state) is critical to our success. **"If you don't know where you're going, you'll probably end up somewhere else."** — *David Campbell, Ph.D.*

PLAN-DO-CHECK-ACT (PDCA)

What is it?

A practical sequence of steps for solving problems.

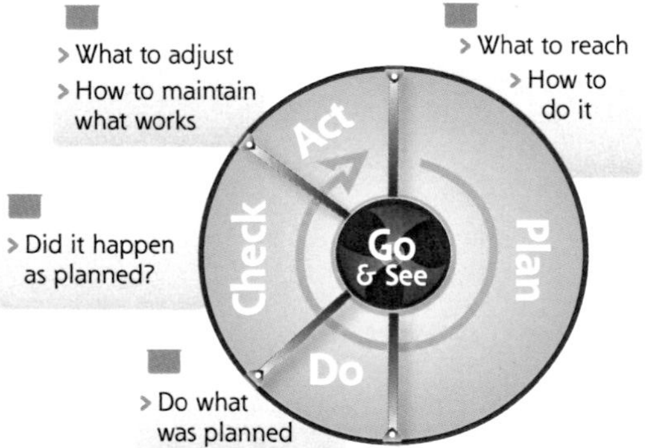

Why use it?

- Effective problem solving
- Prevents you from being satisfied with superficial solutions that won't fix the problem in the long run

How do I do it?

1. **PLAN** what you want to accomplish and what you need to do to get there
2. **DO** what you planned on doing
3. **CHECK** the results of what you did to see if the objective was achieved
4. **ACT/ADJUST** on the information – standardize or plan for further improvement: what is next?

The 8 Steps to Practical Problem Solving

Plan
Plan what you want to accomplish and what you need to get there
1 Clarify the problem
2 Break down the problem
3 Set a target
4 Analyze the root causes
5 Develop countermeasures
Act
Act on the information to standardize or to plan further improvements
8 Standardize success and learn from failures
GO & SEE:
We must go & see what really happens in our workplace
Do
Do what you planned on doing
6 Implement countermeasures
Check
Check the results of what you did to see if the objective was achieved
7 Evaluate results and processes

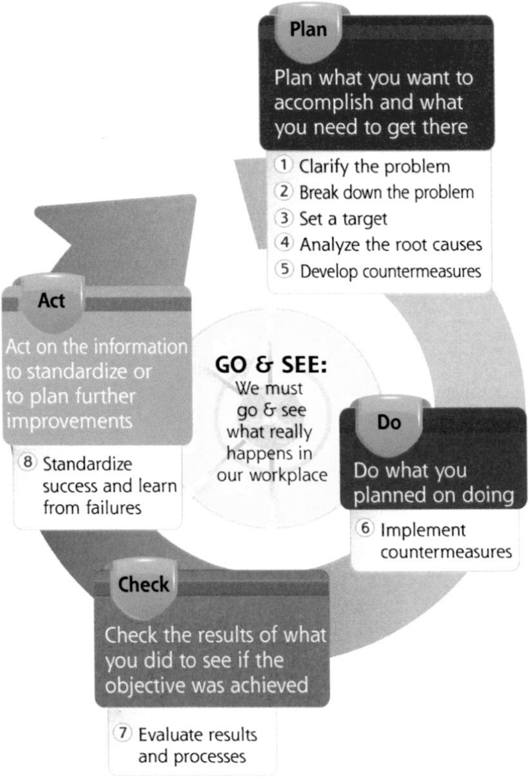

Step 1: *Clarify the problem vs. the ideal state*

- Define and agree on the ideal state (vision).
- Describe the current condition. See with your own eyes in order to get the facts. Ask yourself and others "what is really the problem?" **Use Process Map, SIPOC Diagram, Spaghetti Diagram.**

Step 2: *Break down the problem*

- Break down the problem into smaller, more specific problems. **Use Pareto Chart.**

Step 3: *Set a target*

- Set a target and commit to achieve it. The target should take you one step closer to our ideal state; it does not have to be a huge leap.

Step 4: *Analyze the root causes*

- Identify possible causes which is the starting point of root cause analysis. **Use Fishbone Diagram and 5 Whys.**

Step 5: *Develop countermeasures*

- Brainstorm potential solutions to deal with root cause. Develop an action plan that includes "how, where, who and when."

Step 6: *Implement countermeasures*

- Implement the countermeasures according to the plan. No doubt you will encounter obstacles and challenges, but never give up. Your willingness to persevere will make the difference between success and failure.

Step 7: *Evaluate results and processes*

- Evaluate both the results and the process. Was this an effective countermeasure or just luck?

Step 8: *Standardize success and learn from failures*

- Make the successful countermeasure the new way of doing things and learn from unresolved issues as they can lead to problems.

The A3 Report

What is it?

A one-page document based on the PDCA Cycle. "A3" refers to an international-size paper approximately 11 x 17 inches.

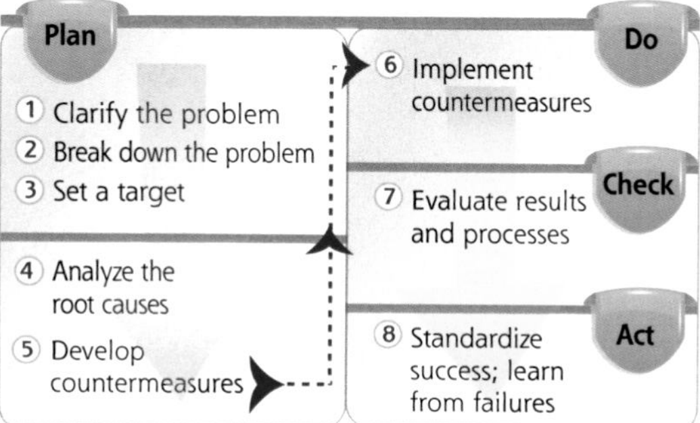

The A3 report is a working document in which the PDCA Cycle is applied to solve a problem, propose solutions, update progress on an ongoing problem or to share implemented solutions.

A3 reports are worked on as a dialogue, not in isolation. Put A3 reports through the eight steps of practical problem solving.

See *The Problem Solving Memory Jogger*™ for more information.

Why use it?

- Avoids vague discussions
- Solves problems systematically by using PDCA

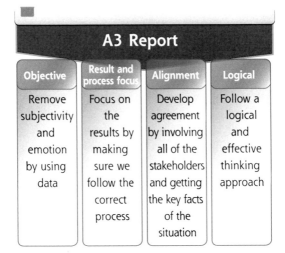

A3 Report

Objective	Result and process focus	Alignment	Logical
Remove subjectivity and emotion by using data	Focus on the results by making sure we follow the correct process	Develop agreement by involving all of the stakeholders and getting the key facts of the situation	Follow a logical and effective thinking approach

The A3 report is a problem-solving tool based on the principle *learn* by doing. Use it to coach others on the 8 steps of practical problem solving by actually solving problems.

"Most people would rather live with a problem they can't solve, than accept a solution they can't understand."
— R.E.D Woolsey and H.S. Swanson

Types of A3 reports

There are three types of A3 reports that you can use to solve a problem following the PDCA cycle:

1. Proposal A3 report
2. Status A3 report
3. Final A3 report

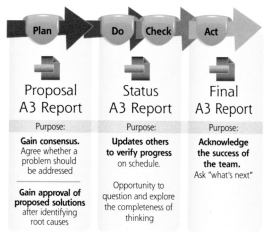

Plan	Do / Check	Act
Proposal A3 Report	**Status A3 Report**	**Final A3 Report**
Purpose:	Purpose:	Purpose:
Gain consensus. Agree whether a problem should be addressed **Gain approval of proposed solutions** after identifying root causes	**Updates others to verify progress** on schedule. Opportunity to question and explore the completeness of thinking	**Acknowledge the success of the team.** Ask "what's next"

In the A3 report, it is the PDCA way of thinking, not conformance to a template that matters the most.

To access a PDF version of the forms in this book, visit **MemoryJogger.org/LSS** for downloadable forms.

A3 Report

OPPORTUNITY:

Location: Date: / /

1. CLARIFY THE PROBLEM

Describe the current condition:

Key metric to impact: ____________

Problem Identification

Who: ____________

What: ____________

Where: ____________

When: ____________

Problem Statement:

Factual, within scope, short and focus on clearly identifying the gap

2. BREAK DOWN THE PROBLEM

Break down the problem into smaller, more specific problems:

Use Process Map, Pareto Chart

Wastes Identified

Transportation [ ]
Inventory [ ]
Motion [ ]
Waiting [ ]
Overproduction [ ]
Over-processing [ ]
Defects [ ]
Skills unused [ ]

3. SET A TARGET (The challenge):

Improve ____________ From ______ to ______ by ______

What (metric) *Current* *Target* *When*

4. ANALYZE THE ROOT CAUSE

Identify the root causes

Fishbone Diagram, 5 Whys

Team member names	Leader	

5 & 6. DEVELOP & IMPLEMENT COUNTERMEASURES

Describe the countermeasures:

Root Causes	Selected Countermeasures	Who	Start	Target	Finish

7. EVALUATE RESULTS

Evaluate the results and process:

Use same metric as in Step 3. Make sure before and after conditions are visible.

8. STANDARDIZE

Means of Standardization:

Standard Work: [ ] Visual Aids: [ ] SOP: [ ] Training: [ ]

Process Audits:

LPA: [ ] TPM Check List: [ ] 5S Audit: [ ] Others: ______ [ ]

Next Challenge:

Further change to sustain improvement

Sharing with Others:

List other groups with whom you shared the project

Lessons Learned:

List two key lessons learned from this project

OPPORTUNITY: To get to work on time

Location:

Date: 5 /10

1. CLARIFY THE PROBLEM

Problem Statement: *Short, measurable*

Arriving late during the last 8 weeks

Facts on current condition

Target = 8 am

Wk1 → Wk8

Key Metric to Impact: Clock-in (time at work)

Problem Identification

What: Arrival time @work

Where: Home & work

When: Every morning

Who: Joe T.

Why: Be fired

2. BREAKDOWN THE PROBLEM

Map the process

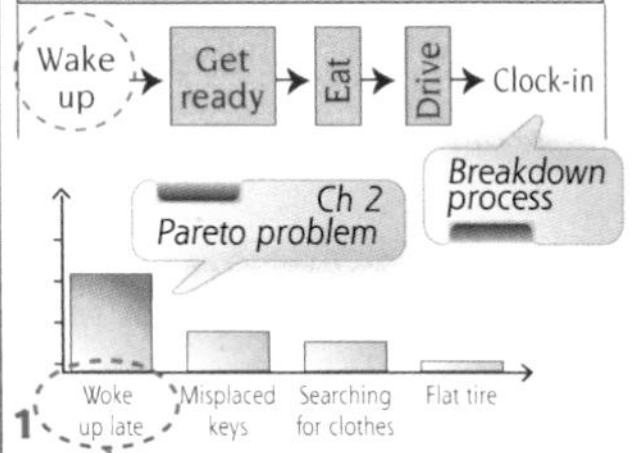

Wastes Identified

Transportation [X]

Inventory [ ]

Motion [X]

Waiting [ ]

Overproduction [ ]

Over-processing [X]

Defects [X]

Skills unused [ ]

Wasteful activities Ch3

3. SET A TARGET (The challenge):

Improve Arrival time to work From 8:24 to 8:00 by 06/10

What (metric) — *Current* — *Target* — *When*

4. ANALYZE THE ROOT CAUSE

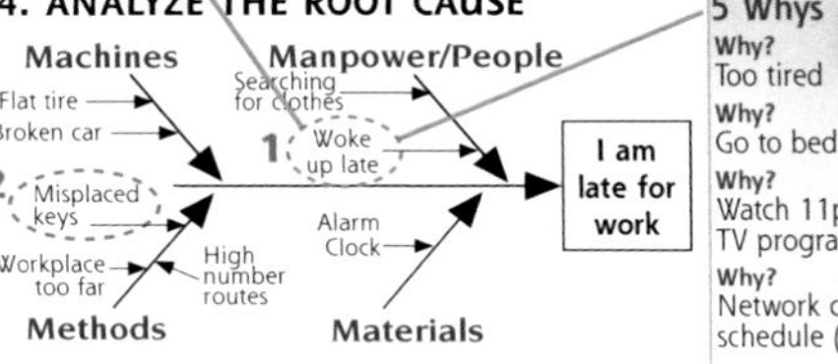

5 Whys — *Ch 2 Ask why*

Why? Too tired

Why? Go to bed too late

Why? Watch 11pm favorite TV program

Why? Network changed schedule (9 to 11pm)

Team member names		
Joe T.	Leader	
Mary T.		

5 & 6. DEVELOP & IMPLEMENT COUNTERMEASURES

Ch 5 Set countermeasures

Root Causes	Selected Countermeasures	Who	Start	Target	Finish
1 Watch late TV show	1.1 Set timer to record TV	Joe T.	05/11	05/11	05/12
	1.2 Watch show before 8pm	Joe T.	05/11	05/11	05/12
	1.3 Be in bed before 9pm	Joe T.	05/11	05/11	05/12
2 No fixed location for keys	2.1 Set a fixed key hook (5S)	Joe T.	05/12	05/12	05/12
	2.2 Share new location with Mary	Joe T.	05/15	05/15	05/15

7. EVALUATE RESULTS

Ch 5 Set countermeasures

Summary of results

100% on time for the last 4 weeks

Evaluate the process

Clock-in (time at work)

Before

After

Target = 8 am

Week 8

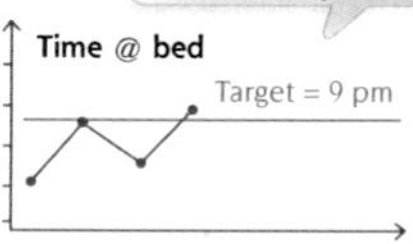

Time @ bed

Target = 9 pm

8. STANDARDIZE

Means of Standardization:

Standard Work: [X] Visual Aids: [ ] SOP: [ ] Training: [ ]

Process Audits:

LPA: [ ] TPM Check List: [ ] 5S Audit: [ ] Others: Checklist [X]

Next Challenge: *Seek ideal state ch7*

Searching for clothes

Sharing with Others: *Share practices ch 7*

Shared with Mary

Lesson Learned: *Reflect Ch 7*

To apply practical problem solving

Pareto Chart

What is it?

A chart that displays occurrences from most frequent to least frequent is usually expressed as a count or a percentage.

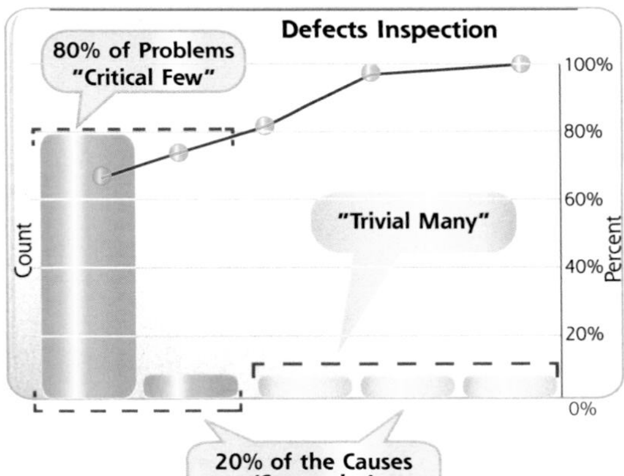

Why use it?

- Breaks down complex problems into components
- Identifies the most significant contributors to a problem
- Communicates your findings with others

Pareto Principle: "80% of the problems come from 20% of the causes."

How do I do it?

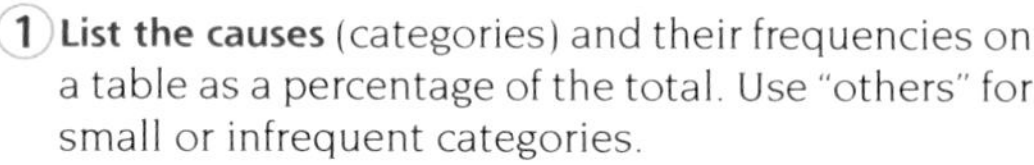

1. **List the causes** (categories) and their frequencies on a table as a percentage of the total. Use "others" for small or infrequent categories.
2. **Arrange categories** by frequency or level of impact or importance of the causes.
3. **Draw a bar for each category,** starting with the largest and working down.
4. **Add in the cumulative** percentage line (optional).

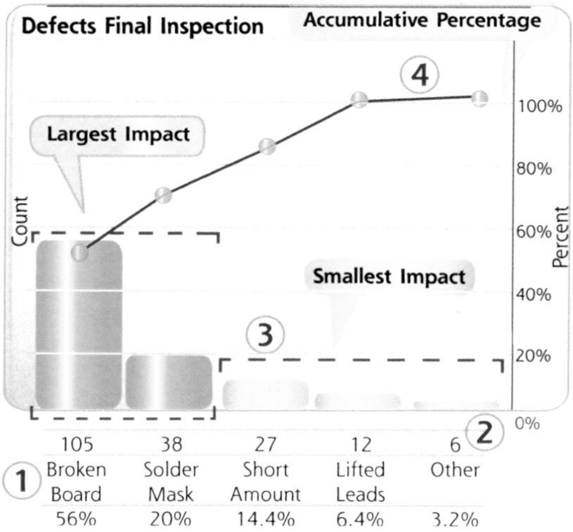

Defects Final Inspection **Accumulative Percentage**

Largest Impact

Smallest Impact

Count

Percent

100%
80%
60%
40%
20%
0%

105	38	27	12	6
Broken Board	Solder Mask	Short Amount	Lifted Leads	Other
56%	20%	14.4%	6.4%	3.2%

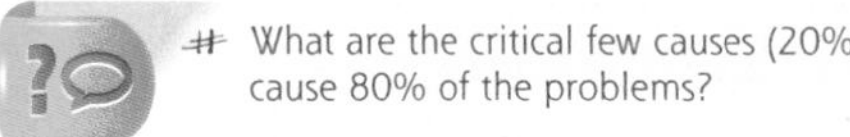

What are the critical few causes (20%) that cause 80% of the problems?

Fishbone Diagram (or Ishikawa Diagram)

What is it?

A map of major possible causes of a particular problem (effect).

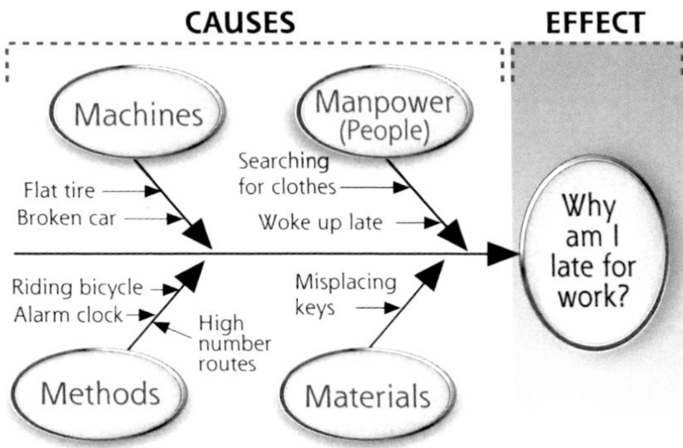

Why use it?

- Provides structure to cause identification effort
- Ensures major possible causes are not overlooked

Common major cause categories to use in the Fishbone Diagram:

4Ms: MACHINES, METHODS, MANPOWER (PEOPLE) & MATERIALS

6Ms: *including* MEASUREMENT & ENVIRONMENT (MOTHER NATURE)

How do I do it?

1. **Name the problem** at the head of a fishbone "skeleton." Be as specific as possible.
2. **Draw the major categories for causes.** Typical categories include the 6 Ms: manpower (people), machines, materials, methods, measurements, and mother nature (or environment).
3. **Brainstorm** for detailed causes by asking "why" each major cause happens (see 5 Whys).
4. **Identify causes** you think are most critical for follow-up investigation.
5. **Confirm** that potential causes are actual causes. *Caution*: do not generate action plans until you've verified the cause.

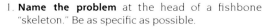

Methods
Measurements
Materials
Cause 1
Cause 5
Cause 2
Cause 3
Cause 4
The Problem
Machines
Mother Nature
Manpower (People)

When dealing with root causes, focus first on the causes within your area of control.

5 Whys

What is it?

Ask "Why" several times to explore the cause/effect relationships underlying a particular problem.

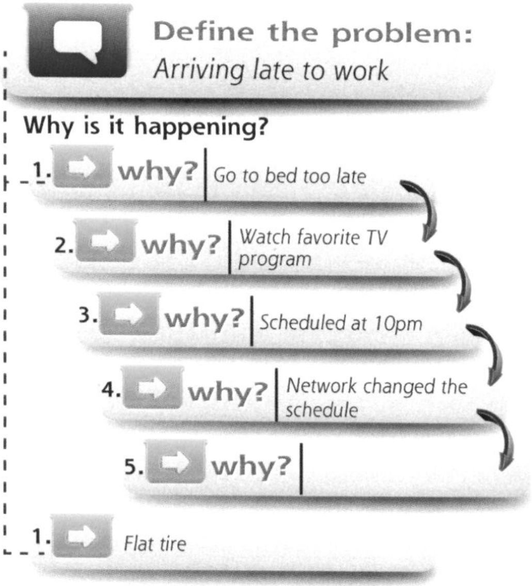

Define the problem:
Arriving late to work

Why is it happening?

1. why? *Go to bed too late*
2. why? *Watch favorite TV program*
3. why? *Scheduled at 10pm*
4. why? *Network changed the schedule*
5. why?

1. *Flat tire*

Apply one countermeasure at a time to clearly **see** the effectiveness of each countermeasure.

Why use it?

- Determines root causes of a defect or problem
- Prevent superficial solutions that won't fix the problem in the long run

How do I do it?

1. Select a cause (from a fishbone diagram or a Pareto chart).
2. Ask "Why does this outcome occur?"
   – "Why 1?"
3. Select one of the reasons for Why 1 and ask "Why does that occur?"
   – "Why 2?"
4. Continue until you feel you have reached a potential root cause.

Asking "Why" five times is not mandatory: You may need to ask more or less times to identify the root cause.

Higher Why

What is it?

An extension of the 5 Whys to evaluate new potential solutions when the perceived problem is too narrow.

5 Whys approach:

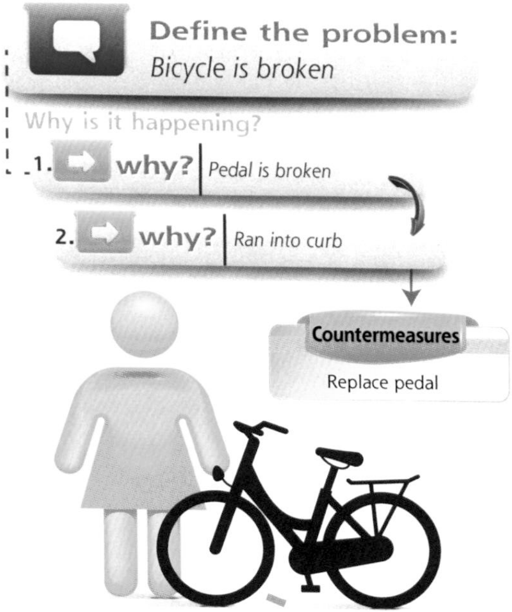

Define the problem:
Bicycle is broken

Why is it happening?

1. **why?** | *Pedal is broken*
2. **why?** | *Ran into curb*

Countermeasures

Replace pedal

Higher Why approach:

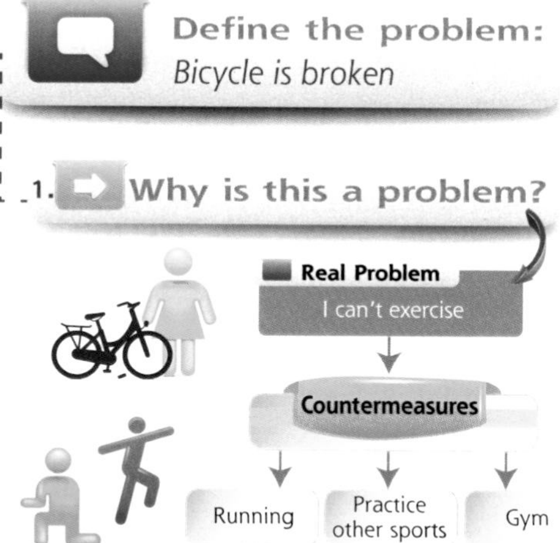

Why use it?

- Introduces new and better alternative countermeasures

How do I do it?

- Ask why the perceived problem is a problem
- Identify the real problem
- Ask *why* to identify possible causes for the higher level problem

5 Whys - 3 Levels

What is it?

A deeper approach of 5 Whys to look for root causes by examining three levels.

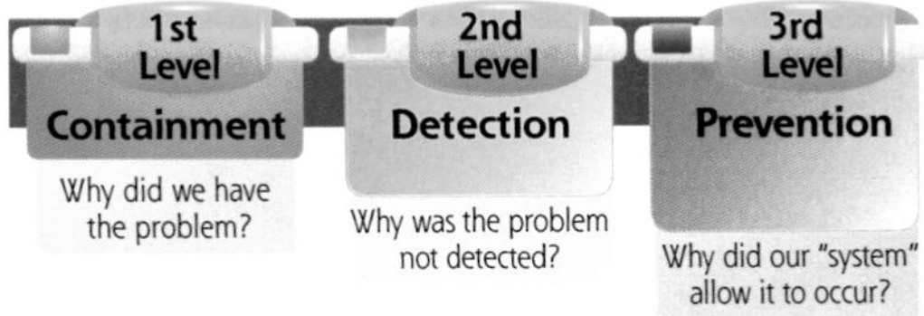
1st Level
Containment
Why did we have the problem?
2nd Level
Detection
Why was the problem not detected?
3rd Level
Prevention
Why did our "system" allow it to occur?

Problem: Late payment fee on my credit card bill

First level: Containment

1. Why? I didn't pay on time
   2. Why? I forgot the due date
      3. Why? I didn't write down the due date

   Solution: **Write down the due date**

Second level: Detection

Why didn't I detect past due dates?
   I don't periodically check my accounts.
   Solution: **Review accounts once a week**

Third level: Prevention

Why did the system allow the problem to occur?
   It relies on remembering due dates.
   Solution: **Have all due dates in a calendar**

Why use it?

Leads to approach problems in a systematic way instead of looking at them as isolated events.

Chapter THREE

Define Value

Counter-measures

Define Value CHAPTER 3

- Value-Added Work
- The 8 Deadly Wastes
- 3Ms Waste
  Overburden
  Variation

Seek Ideal State CHAPTER 7

- Reflection
- Sharing Practices

Develop People

Observe Entire Value Stream CHAPTER 4

- Value Stream Mapping
- Process Map
- SIPOC
- Spaghetti Diagram
- Takt Time

Let Customers Pull CHAPTER 6

- Kanban

Make Value-Added Steps Flow CHAPTER 5

- Visual Management
- 5S
- Mistake-Proofing
- Standard Work
- One-Piece Flow
- Cellular Layout
- Line Balancing
- Quick Changeover
- Total Productive Maintenance
- Layered Process Audit

Value-Added Work

What is value?

Three conditions must be present for any activity to be considered value added:

- The customer must be willing to pay for it
- A change in form, fit or function of the product or service
- The change or transformation must be done right the first time

If any of these conditions is missing, the activity or process step is **Non-value-added or Waste.**

Around 5-10% of what we do is value-added work for our customers
Activity that is entirely unnecessary in achieving the objective of the operation
VALUE-ADDED WORK
WASTE
DAILY WORK
OPERATION
NON-VALUE-ADDED
Non-value-added activity that cannot be skipped under the current constraint

The 8 Deadly Wastes

What is it?

Any activity that does not add value from the customers' perspective and can be eliminated. Initially identified by Taiichi Ohno, the 8 deadly wastes are a practical way to recognize waste.

Use the mnemonic "TIM WOODS" to remember them:

TIMWOODS

1 Waste — TRANSPORTATION
> Any nonessential transport is waste

2 Waste — INVENTORY
> Any more than the minimum to get the job done

3 Waste — MOTION
> Any motion that does not add value

4 Waste — WAITING
> Waiting on parts or for a machine to finish cycle

5 Waste — OVERPRODUCTION
> Producing too much or too soon

6 Waste — OVER-PROCESSING
> Any more than required by the customer

7 Waste — DEFECTS
> Any repair

8 Waste — SKILLS UNUSED
> Any failure to fully utilize the time/talents of people

Why use it?

- To see or identify wasteful activities around us

90–95% of any typical process is non-value-added or waste. Can you identify activities that do not add value to your customers?

TIMWOODS

Transportation Movement of materials using carts, conveyors, forklifts or simply your arms and legs.

Inventory Material or work on-hand other than what's needed right now to satisfy customer demand.

Motion Movement of people that does not add value.

Waiting Idle time when people, materials, information or equipment is not available when required. Less visible than other wastes because it is often replaced by "busy work."

Overproduction Producing more products or information than the customer requires. The worst of the wastes because it causes most of the other wastes.

Over-processing When operations create non-value from the customer's perspective.

Defects Any product or service that does not meet customer's specifications or steps to correct these defects (hidden factory).

Skills unused The waste of human potential. People in every organization have great ideas. Leaving those ideas untapped by not engaging or listening is certainly wasteful.

Three Ms—Waste (Muda), Overburden (Muri), Variation (Mura)

What is it?

The **three targets** LEO focuses on to eliminate:

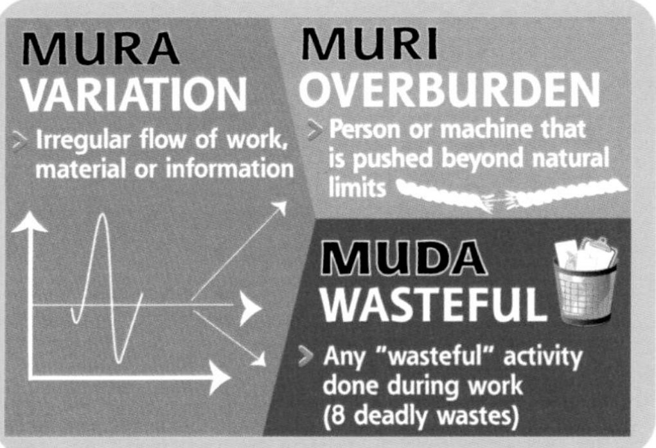

MURA
VARIATION
Irregular flow of work, material or information
MURI
OVERBURDEN
Person or machine that is pushed beyond natural limits
MUDA
WASTEFUL
Any "wasteful" activity done during work (8 deadly wastes)

Focusing only on the 8 deadly wastes is not enough, the objective is to eliminate all three Ms: wasteful activities, variation and overburden.

Examples:

- **Variation:** Irregular production schedule
- **Overburden:** Machine breakdown for lack of maintenance

When **overburden** or **Muri** is ignored, you create safety and quality problems (people) and breakdown and defects (equipment).

Why use it?

To identify the sources of wasteful activities

How do I do it?

1. Stand and observe the activity. Do not ask or engage in discussion
2. Write down the small problems or types of waste that you observe
3. Identify the type of waste for each of your findings
4. Look for the root cause with your team members of the most critical findings by asking "why" several times
   - Identify the sources of variation (Mura) that make the flow of work, material or information irregular: Why does the flow vary between processes? How can the flow be leveled?
5. Identify countermeasures to create flow. Review Chapter 5, Make Value-Added Steps Flow

Mura or variation creates conditions where people and machines are overburdened at times and under-utilized at other times. Mura can be seen as a source of Muri and Muda.

See *The Lean Enterprise Memory Jogger*™ for more information on the 3Ms.

Chapter FOUR

Observe the Entire Value Stream

Counter-measures
Define Value
CHAPTER 3
> Value-Added Work
> The 8 Deadly Wastes
> 3Ms Waste
Overburden
Variation
Seek Ideal State
CHAPTER 7
> Reflection
> Sharing Practices
Observe Entire Value Stream
CHAPTER 4
> Value Stream Mapping
> Process Map
> SIPOC
> Spaghetti Diagram
> Takt Time
Let Customers Pull
CHAPTER 6
> Kanban
Make Value-Added Steps Flow
CHAPTER 5
> Visual Management
> 5S
> Mistake-Proofing
> Standard Work
> One-Piece Flow
> Cellular Layout
> Line Balancing
> Quick Changeover
> Total Productive Maintenance
> Layered Process Audit

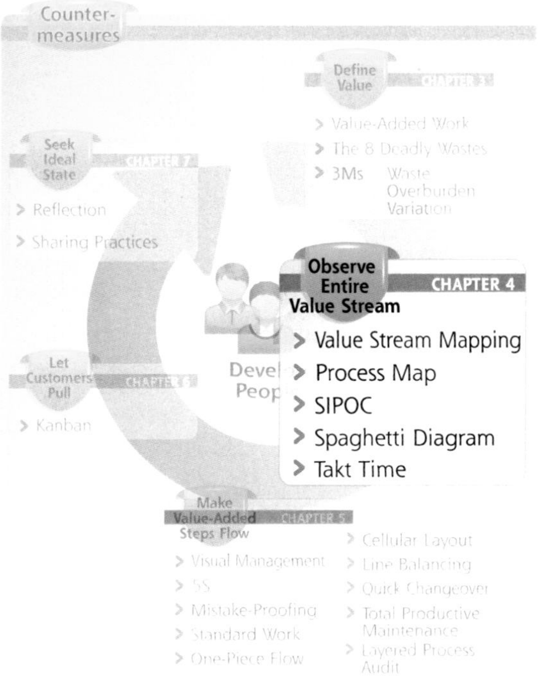

What is a Value Stream?

A sequence of activities, value added, non-value added, and waste, required to produce a product or service.

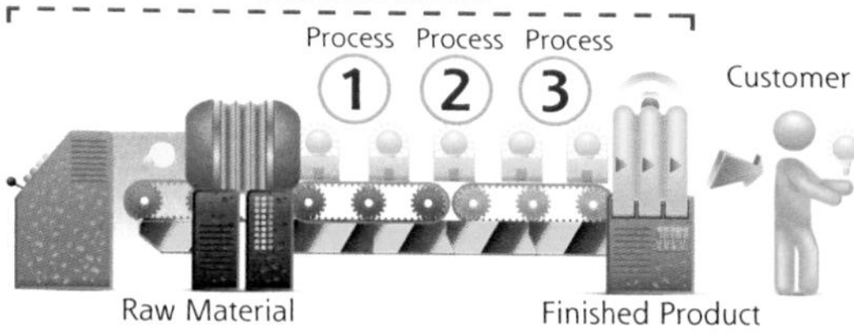

What is a value stream map?

A graphic representation of the material and information (decision) flow from beginning to end.

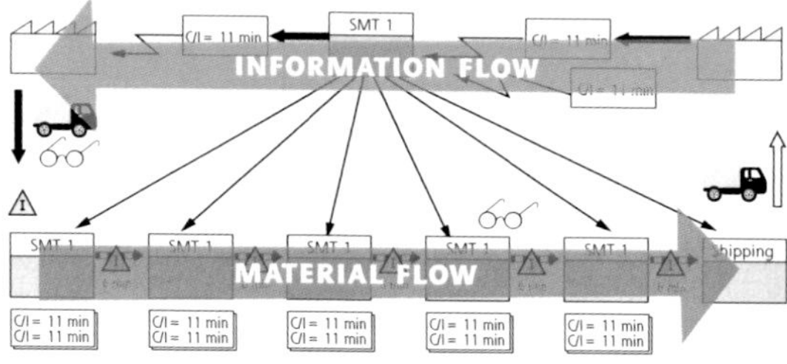

Why use it?

- Helps identify the source of waste to eliminate it
- Shows the linkage between the information flow (decisions) and the material flow
- Creates a common vision of the changes (future state) and the plan to achieve them

Types of Value Stream Maps

1. **Extended or Enterprise:** When the entire value creation flow is mapped, including suppliers' and customers' material and information flow
2. **Door-to-door or Factory:** When only the steps within a factory or site are mapped (e.g., from receiving to shipping)
3. **Process:** When a specific process or processes within a factory or site are mapped

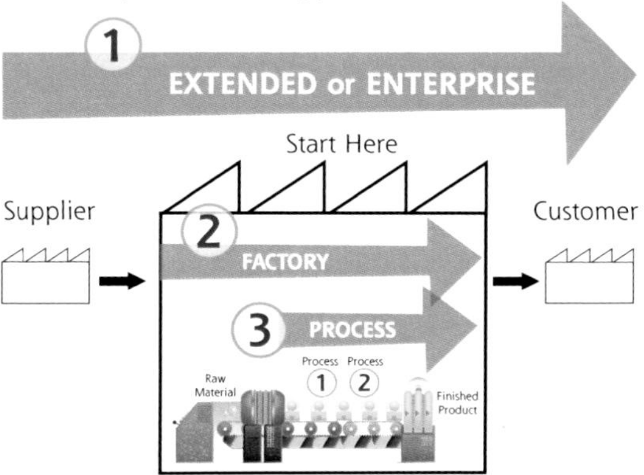

What is the difference between Value Stream Map and other process maps?

Value Stream Maps will always provide both material and information flow while other process maps usually don't include the information flow.

Value Stream Mapping - Both material & information flow

Process Map - MISSING information flow

How to use Value Stream Mapping

PROCESS STEPS & EQUIPMENT (1)

PRODUCTS / PROCESS	Step 1	Step 2	Step 3	Step 4	Step 5	Step 6	Step 7	Step 8	Step 9	Step 10	Step 11	Step 12
1	X	X	X	X				X		X	X	X
2	X											
3	X				X	X	X	X	X	X	X	X
4	X	X	X	X				X		X	X	X
5	X	X	X	X				X		X	X	X

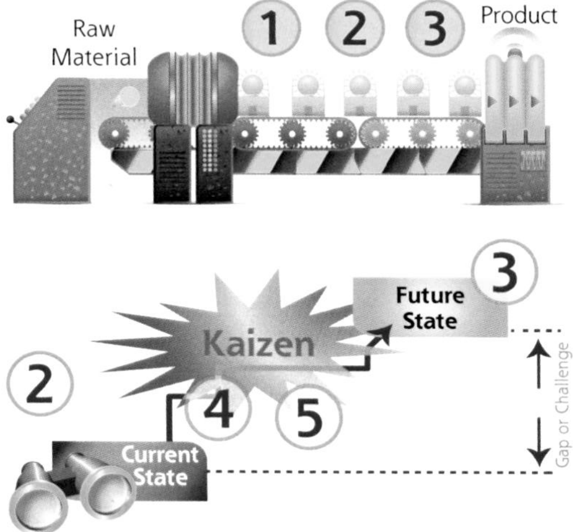

1. **Select the target product family or service** and identify the sponsor (who can make decisions, arbitrate solutions and prioritize resources) and team (ensuring that each area or stakeholder of the process is represented).

2. **Create a current state map.** Draw a current state value stream map to understand how things currently operate. Walk the process from end to end.

3. **Create a future state map.** Define the vision to becoming leaner in terms of creating flow by eliminating waste.

4. **Create an implementation plan to reach the future state.**

5. **Do Kaizen events and projects** to achieve the future state.

Don't be intimidated with these upcoming symbols and their meaning as you apply Value Stream Mapping. Use them as you need them. If necessary, create or modify them to better represent your reality but keep it simple.

See *The Lean Enterprise Memory Jogger*™ for more information on value stream mapping.

What do the symbols represent?

Material Sources

Symbol	Name	Description
	Outside Sources	Represents the supplier and customer
	Process	A process, operation, machine or department through which material flows
CT = C/O = Yield = Uptime =	Data Box	Used for processes that have significant information/data required for analyzing and observing the system
I	Inventory	Used to show inventory quantities between two processes
	Truck Shipment	Shipments from suppliers or to customers using external transport
	Push Arrow	The "pushing" of material from one process to the next
Max. ___ FIFO	FIFO Lane	First-in-First-Out inventory. Use this icon when processes are connected with FIFO system that limits input
	Super-market	An inventory "supermarket" or kanban stock point
	Material Pull	Supermarkets connect to downstream processes with this "pull" icon that indicates physical removal

Information Symbols

Symbol	Name	Description
	Manual Information Flow	Flow of information from memos, reports, or conversations. Frequently, other notes may be relevant
	Electronic Information Flow	Such as electronic data interchange (EDI), the internet, intranets, local area network (LAN), wide area network (WAN)

Information Symbols *Continued*

Symbol	Name	Description
	"Go See" Scheduling	Gathering of information through visual means
	Information	Describes an information flow
OXOX	Load Leveling	A tool to batch kanbans in order to level the production volume and mix over a period of time
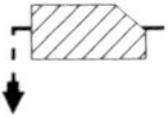	With-drawal Kanban	A card or device that instructs a material handler to transfer parts from a supermarket to the receiving process
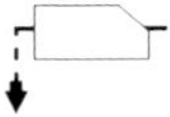	Production Kanban	Triggers production of a pre-defined number of parts. The one-per-container kanban.It signals a supplying process to provide parts to a downstream process
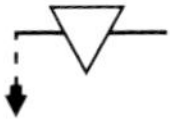	Signal Kanban	The "one-per-batch" kanban signals when a reorder point is reached and another batch needs to be produced
	Kanban Post	A location where kanban signals reside for pickup

General Symbols

Symbol	Name	Description
	Kaizen Burst	Improvement needs and planned kaizen workshops in specific processes that are critical to achieving the future state map of the value stream
	Buffer or Safety Stock	Inventory to protect the system against internal problems (Safety Stock) or sudden fluctuations in customer orders (Buffer). Buffer or Safety Stock must be noted

Process Map

What is it?

Any diagram that describes the material, people or information flow or a combination of them in the creation of a product or service.

Process maps can be used to represent current or expected conditions of a process.

Why use it?

- Makes it easy to "see" and understand the flow of material, people and/or information

How do I do it?

Use this table to decide which process map to use.

Process Map	Objective
IPO (Input-Process-Output) or SIPOC (Supplier-Input-Process-Output–Customer) Diagrams	Provide a big picture understanding of the process. Usually used for project scoping purposes
Flow Chart	Present a more detailed level of the process steps and their connections
Swim-lane Chart	Identify interaction of the departments or people involved in the process
Spaghetti Diagram	Present the material and/or people flow through the physical layout
Value Stream Map or Material and Information Flow Diagram	Map the material and information flow at high level

SIPOC Diagram

What is it?

A high-level chart that describes the five components of any value creation chain: Supplier, Input, Process, Output and Customer.

Why use it?

- Makes it easy to "see" and scope the value creation chain.

How do I do it?

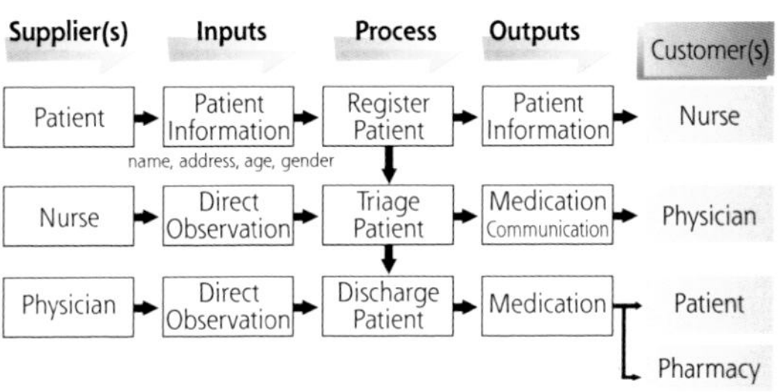

- Identify key processes: Keep at a high level, with perhaps 6 activities at most.
- Identify the key outputs and customers of those outputs: If you have a lot of different outputs and customers, focus on the critical few.
- Identify inputs and suppliers: If you have a lot of different inputs and customers, focus on the critical few.
- Identify critical requirements for the inputs, process steps, and outputs.

Spaghetti Diagram

What is it?

A chart of the material and/or people-flow through the physical layout required to create a product or service.

Why use it?

- Makes it easy to "see" the opportunities for improvement in people and material flow

How do I do it?

Draw current state

1. **Create a diagram of the physical layout** related to the process you are improving.
2. **Draw lines following the sequence** of the process steps of information, material, and people.

Improved state

3. **Discuss the current state spaghetti diagram** to create a cleaner flow by asking:
   - Can process steps be eliminated, simplified or combined?
   - Can process steps flow in clusters together to eliminate motion and transportation?

The name Spaghetti Diagram comes from how the flow usually looks like spaghetti in a bowl.

Spaghetti Diagram (Before)

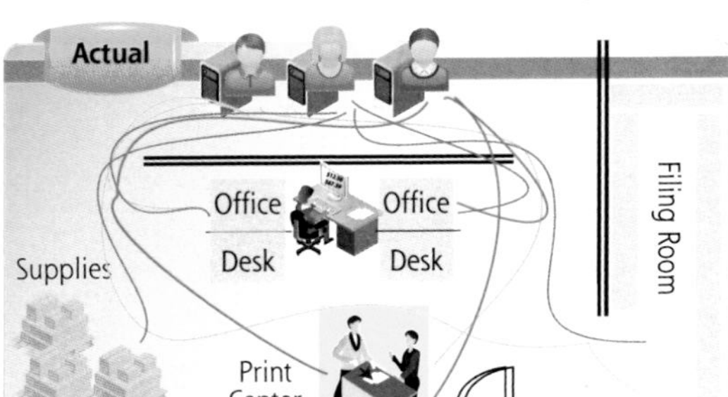

Spaghetti Diagram (After)

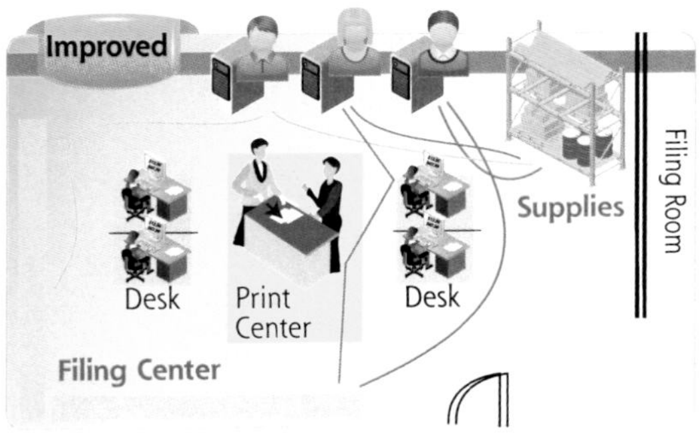

Takt Time

What is it?

The time needed to produce one quality part to meet customer demand. It is calculated as:

$$\text{Takt Time} = \frac{\text{Effective working time per shift}}{\text{Customer requirement per shift}}$$

Why use it?

- Aligns manufacturing rate to demand rate
- Prevents waste

How do I do it?

1. Calculate effective working time per shift

Example: Shift: 6:00am to 2:30pm with 20 minute lunch and 10 minute break. 10 minute daily staff meeting. 5 minutes 5S cleaning workstation.

Total shift time:	8.5 hrs	= 510 min.
Minus lunch time & breaks	510 – 20 – 10	= 480 min.
Minus set-up and mainten.	480 – 10 – 5	= 465 min.
Effective working time:		= 465 min.
		= 27,900 sec.

*Do **NOT** subtract **unscheduled** downtime*

2. Calculate customer requirement for shift

Example:
Demand: 1300 units per day. 1 shift per day

Customer requirement = 1,300 units

3. Calculate Takt time

$$\text{Takt Time: } \frac{27{,}900 \text{ sec}}{1{,}300 \text{ units}} = 21 \text{ sec}$$

"Every 21 seconds we need to produce a unit to meet our customer demand"

Chapter FIVE

Make Value-Added Steps Flow

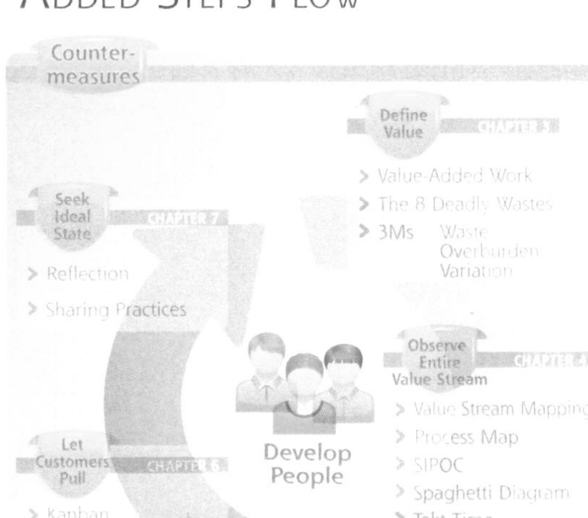

Make Value-Added Steps Flow CHAPTER 5

- Visual Management
- 5S
- Mistake-Proofing
- Standard Work
- One-Piece Flow
- Cellular Layout
- Line Balancing
- Quick Changeover
- Total Productive Maintenance
- Layered Process Audit

VISUAL MANAGEMENT

What is it?

Simple controls to:

- **Make normal and abnormal conditions visible** so standards can easily be followed by all employees.
- **Make waste visible** so you can eliminate it and prevent it from recurring in the future.

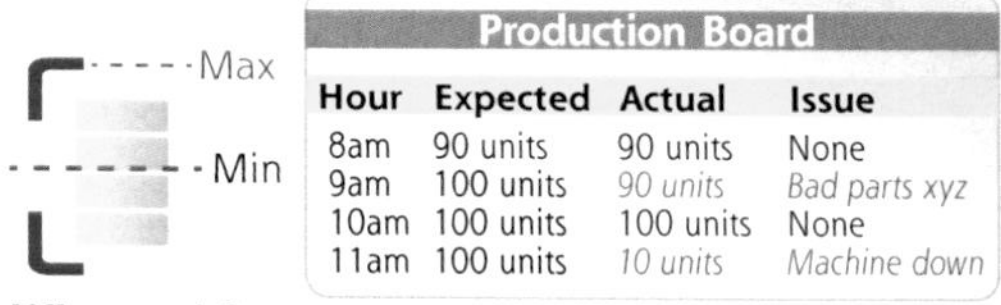

Max
Min
Production Board
Hour Expected Actual Issue
8am 90 units 90 units None
9am 100 units 90 units Bad parts xyz
10am 100 units 100 units None
11am 100 units 10 units Machine down

Why use it?

- Simple and effective way to communicate standards, expectations, and information in general

How do I do it?

Implementing Visual Management requires three steps:

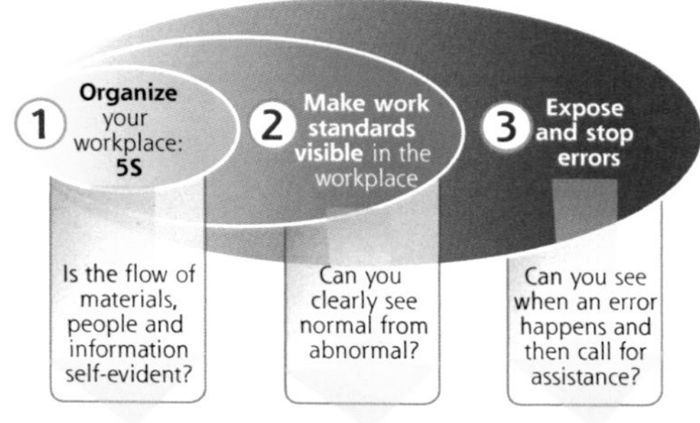

5S Methodology

What is it?

A 5-step methodology to create and maintain an organized workplace to focus on creating uninterrupted flow of material, people and information.

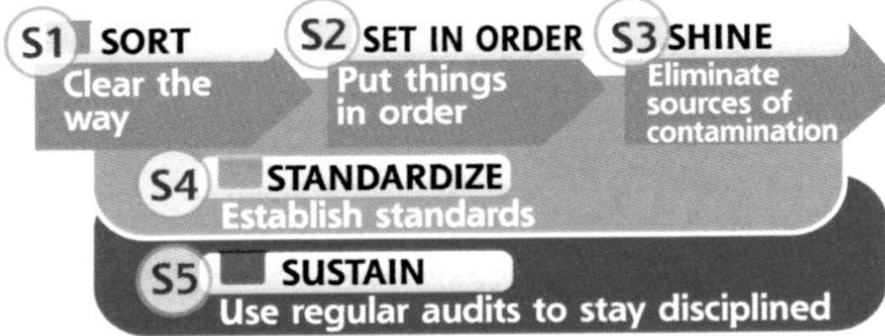

Why use it?

- Enables anyone to distinguish between normal and abnormal conditions at a glance

How do I do it?

Organize a cross-functional team (including team members from the target area)

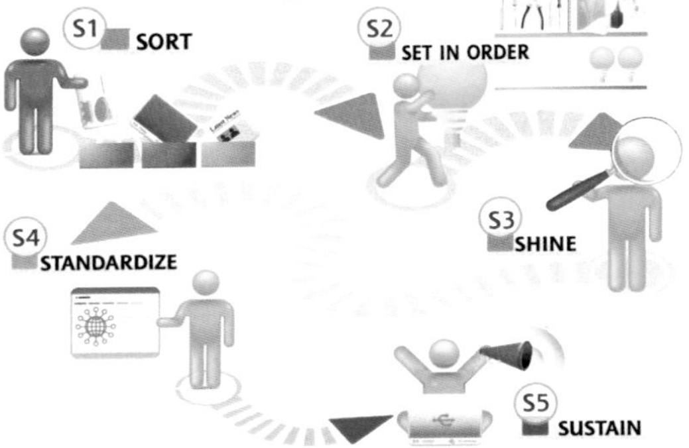

BEFORE 5S

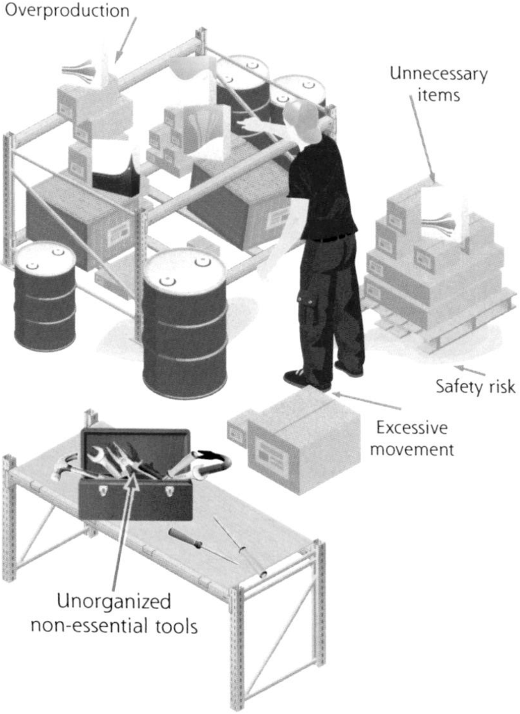

Overproduction

Unnecessary items

Safety risk

Excessive movement

Unorganized non-essential tools

AFTER 5S

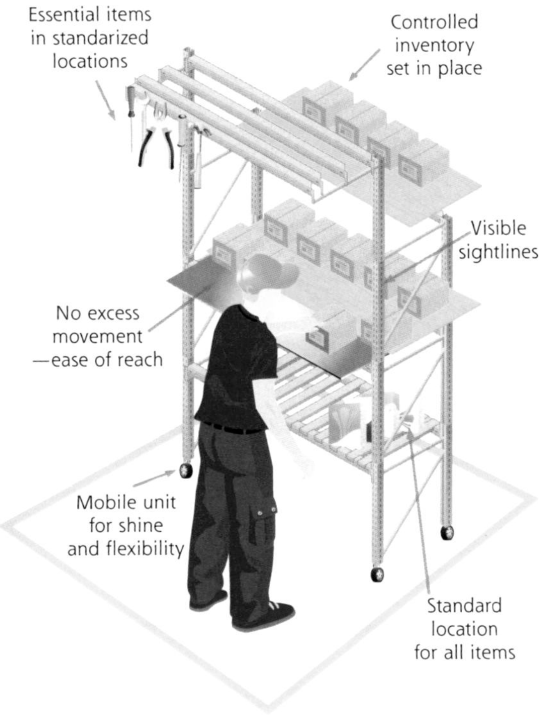

Essential items in standarized locations

Controlled inventory set in place

Visible sightlines

No excess movement —ease of reach

Mobile unit for shine and flexibility

Standard location for all items

How do I implement it?

1. **Define criteria for sorting** items based on their usefulness, frequency and quantity needed. Key questions for each item:

Do we use this item?

How many units do we use each day, week, and month?

How often do we use it?

2. **Define and make red tags** to identify the unneeded items

3. **Conduct "red tag sessions"** by sorting and attaching red tags to potential unneeded items and keeping a log of red tagged items

4. **Evaluate red tagged items** by involving people familiar with the process:
   - Dispose of unnecessary items
   - Move remaining red tagged items to holding area

Key question in SORT: "Do you really need this?"

RED TAG

#

Not used in last week/month

Will not be used in next week/month

Date tag attached

Date action was taken

> Item description

>Item identification number

> Quantity

Number of units

> Reason for tagging

Unnecessary

Too many

Defective

> Action

Scrap

Return to

Dispose

Move to storage

How do I implement it?

1. **Understand the flow of materials, people and information**
   - Observe and map the current process.
   - Identify motion & transportation caused by poor location of equipment, tools and materials.
2. **Define a better workplace**
   - Aim to achieve minimum body motion and effort.
   - Set the 3Fs standard: **FIXED location, FIXED item, FIXED quantity**
3. **Visually organize the workplace** by:
   - Drawing borders to differentiate work areas and paths such as traffic lanes, mobile equipment location.
   - Identifying each item and bordered area to show where and how much material should be kept in a specific place.

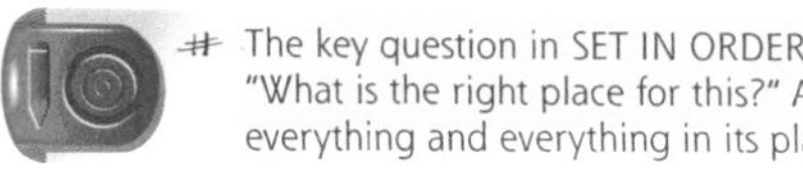

The key question in SET IN ORDER is: "What is the right place for this?" A place for everything and everything in its place.

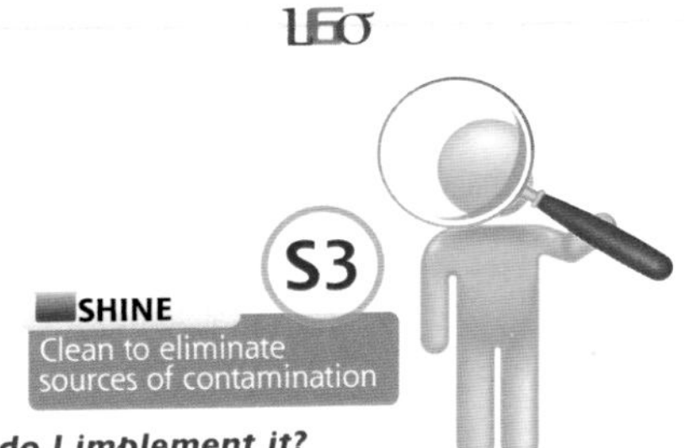

How do I implement it?

1. **Explain the needs for a clean workplace:** prevent accidents (spills on the floor), more efficient and effective work (reaching for tools), protect equipment, tools and material.

2. **Clean to identify, prevent and eliminate sources of contamination and defects** to keep your workplace clean at all times.

3. **Set cleaning responsibilities and frequency**

> Task	> Assigned to	> Frequency
Clean bench	John Miller	Daily
Wipe machine 1 top and down to check for leaks front and back	John Miller	Weekly (Monday)
Check for any loose nuts or bolts at machine 2	John Miller	Monthly (first Monday)

"S3: Shine" is cleaning with the goal of eliminating the need to clean. Avoid cleaning by removing sources of contamination.

S4
STANDARDIZE
Define who, when and how often you should do the first 3Ss

How do I implement it?

1. **Define procedures** to maintain the results from the first 3Ss
   - How should you SORT unnecessary items?
   - How should you SET IN ORDER?
   - How should you SHINE?
2. **Make the procedure visually obvious** to all
   - Make it easier to understand and to know immediately when 5S is slipping.

3Fs STANDARD

FIXED location
FIXED item
FIXED quantity

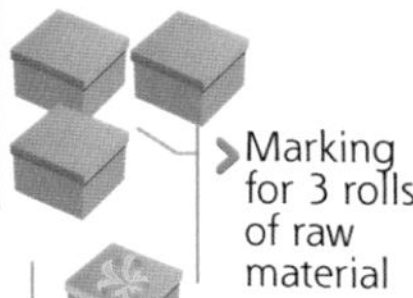
Marking for 3 rolls of raw material
Roll out of marking. Make abnormalities visually evident

"Where there is no standard, there can be no improvement."

S5
SUSTAIN
Evaluate your 5S system periodically. Celebrate successes

How do I implement it?

1. **Involve everyone** by setting evaluations (audits) for your 5S system
   - Daily for associates
   - Weekly for supervisors
   - Monthly for management
2. **Share 5S best practices** while auditing to continuously improve
3. **Link business results to 5S performance**
4. **Celebrate accomplishments**

	Feature	Rating
S1	Are there unused or defective items in the work area? For example: tools, aids, test equipment	
S2	Location and quantities for material, equipment and tools are clearly marked in the work area. Can you recognize where something is located or when something is missing?	
S3	Is the work area free from contamination? For example: through oil, lubrication, waste, paper	
S4	Are there visual standards for S1, S2, and S3 in the work area? For example: color code locations, cleaning schedules, identified areas?	
S5	Are the standards in S4 periodically audited and comprehensively maintained?	

Mistake Proofing (Poka-yoke)

What is it?

Simple devices intended to achieve **mistake-free processes** by preventing errors from occurring in the first place, or detecting errors in the process as early as possible.

BEFORE	**AFTER Using Mistake Proofing**
Parts can be assembled in the wrong direction	Parts can only be assembled in the right direction

Why use it?

- Stops defects from passing into the next process.
- Avoids wasting people skills by designing "smart" processes.

How do I do it?

Organize a cross-functional team (including team members from the target area)

1. Recognize that inspection alone can never achieve zero defects. Errors can be prevented.
2. Look for the sources of defects (root cause) and opportunities to eliminate them at their source.

The goal of mistake proofing is ZERO DEFECTS. Manual inspection is only 90% effective.

3. Understand cause-effect between errors and defects. Errors are the causes of defects.
4. Detail current standard work and work to eliminate any deviations from the standard.
5. Identify the red flag conditions that allow errors.

Red flag conditions

(potential source of errors)

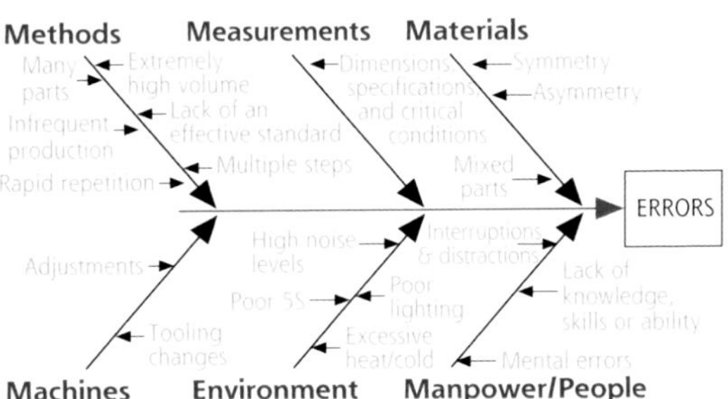

6. Create alternative mistake-proofing solutions. Aim to prevent (most desirable) or detect the error.
7. Implement and select the solution based on the following criteria:
   - Is it cost effective?
   - Is it simple and easy to implement?
   - Is it specifically focused on the problem at hand?
   - Is a cross-functional team developing it?

Standard Work

What is it?

Description of actions performed by people and machines carrying out value-added work in an efficient way, in the right sequence and time, using the right tools.

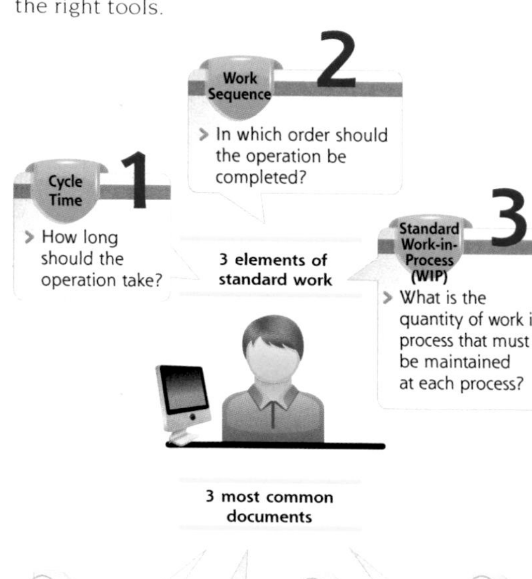
Work Sequence
2
> In which order should the operation be completed?
Cycle Time
1
> How long should the operation take?
3 elements of standard work
Standard Work-in-Process (WIP)
3
> What is the quantity of work in process that must be maintained at each process?
3 most common documents
1
Standard work sheet
2
Standard work combination table
3
Operator instruction or work instruction

STANDARD WORK SHEET

New/Rev. New | Page 1 of 1 | Date: 01/ 02 | Operator: Marilene Moreli

Organization:	Area:	Supervisor:	Product/Service Line: N/A
HMA Assis	Admission	Amelia Padua	Product/Service Name: Outpatient

1. Access "Scheduled Procedure" Report
2. Print "Scheduled Procedure" Report
3. Get "Scheduled Procedure" Report from 'Shared Printer'
4. Place report on Dashboard
5. Get patient's phone number from system
6. Call patient and get insurance information
7. Prepare insurance pre-authorization (5 patients)
8. Fax pre-authorization to insurance company
9. Check fax for pre-authorization forms
10. File pre-authorization forms
11. Call patient to confirm scheduled procedure
12. Update "Scheduled Procedure" in the system
13. Update "Scheduled Procedure" on the Dashboard

DASHBOARD
13
4
Fax Machine
8 9
5 Forms
1
11
7 2 5 7 12 6
Shared Printer
File Cabinet
10
3

Scope of operation	Quality check	Safety precaution	Work-in-progress	Total Manual & Travel Time
From: Unregistered To: Registered				Operator 1 Man/Travel Time 25 min Takt Time: 5 mins

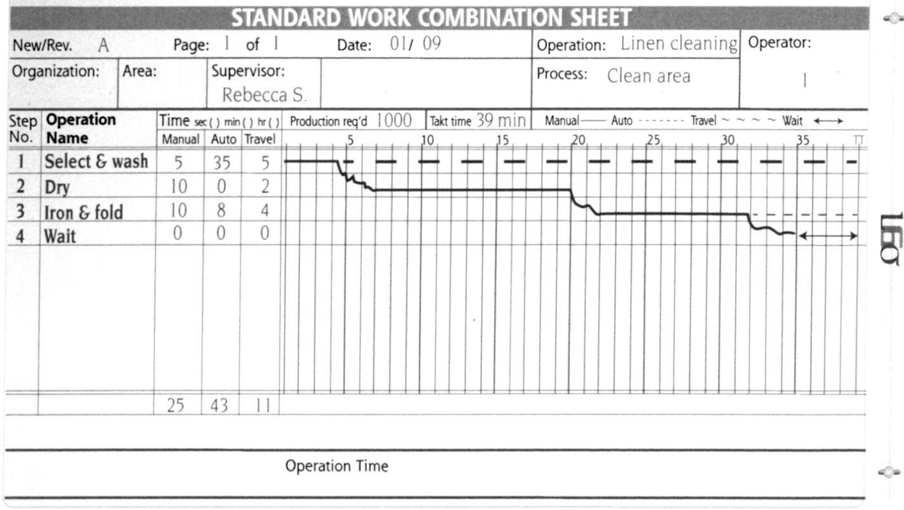

STANDARD WORK COMBINATION SHEET

New/Rev. A | Page: 1 of 1 | Date: 01/09 | Operation: Linen cleaning | Operator: 1

Organization: | Area: | Supervisor: Rebecca S. | Process: Clean area

Production req'd 1000 | Takt time 39 min | Manual —— Auto - - - - - - - Travel ~ ~ ~ ~ Wait ⟷

Step No.	Operation Name	Time sec ( ) min ( ) hr ( ) Manual	Auto	Travel
1	Select & wash	5	35	5
2	Dry	10	0	2
3	Iron & fold	10	8	4
4	Wait	0	0	0
		25	43	11

OPERATOR INSTRUCTION OR WORK INSTRUCTION

Department: Reception   Area: Admission   Operator: 1   Service Type: Outpatient   Prepared by: Alexandre

No.	OPERATION SEQUENCE	KEY POINTS
1.	Access "Scheduled Procedure" Report	From computer
2.	Print "Scheduled Procedure" Report	Use printer HT-6300
3.	Get "Scheduled Procedure" Report from 'Shared Printer'	
4.	Place report on Dashboard	Left top corner
5.	Get patient's phone number from system	Alphabetical order
6.	Call patient and get insurance information	
7.	Prepare insurance pre-authorization (5 patients)	
8.	Fax pre-authorization to insurance company	1-800 number
9.	Check fax for pre-authorization forms	Each 2 hours
10.	File pre-authorization forms	Cabinet TSI-5400
11.	Call patient to confirm scheduled procedure	From 9am to 12pm
12.	Update "Scheduled Procedure" in the system	
13.	Update "Scheduled Procedure" on the Dashboard	

RECORD OF CHANGE			SAFETY CONSIDERATIONS	SIGNATURES			
Date	Rev. Change Description	Supervisor		Date	Shift	Sup.	Operator Initials
01/02	A.B.	C. D.	None	01/02	3	A.P.	M.V.

Why use it?

- Exposes problems (deviations from standard)
- Makes operation rules explicit
- Defines a baseline for future improvement

How do I do it?

Standard work is part of the ongoing cycle to improve processes:

Cycle of Improvement

1 Standardize

> Start with studying the current operation and standardize work procedures, then train operators

2 Expose Problems

> DISPLAY VISUALLY the standard condition so deviations from the standard will be obvious, exposing problems. Audit regularly to check whether the standards are being followed, and if not, then why

3 Solve Problems

> Solve problems by developing improved methods and implementing them

4 Implement a new Method

> Implement the improved method. If the new method is satisfactory, continue the cycle again

Standard work aims to create the most consistent performance possible as the basis for process stability.

One-piece flow

What is it?

The ideal state of efficient operations, where batch sizes are replaced by working on one unit at a time and passing each piece to the next process without delay, and only when it is requested.

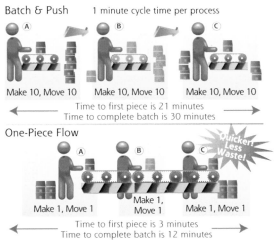

Batch & Push 1 minute cycle time per process

A B C

Make 10, Move 10 Make 10, Move 10 Make 10, Move 10

Time to first piece is 21 minutes
Time to complete batch is 30 minutes

One-Piece Flow

Quicker! Less Waste!

A B C

Make 1, Move 1 Make 1, Move 1 Make 1, Move 1

Time to first piece is 3 minutes
Time to complete batch is 12 minutes

Why use it?

- **Reduces lead time.** The lead time or time required to produce a unit from start to end, decreases as units don't need to queue and wait.

Continuous flow is also commonly referred to as "one-piece flow" or "make one, move one."

- **Makes the defects visible much sooner.** With batch flow, defects are only discovered when all the units of the batch are at the last step and when all units are incorrectly completed.

- **Eliminates waste.** Since one-piece flow is producing only what is needed and when it's needed, overproduction, unnecessary inventory, movement, transportation and other types of waste will decrease.

How do I do it?

Creating One-Piece Flow is a journey. Trying to implement it when processes are not ready will cause more harm than good.

Creating One-Piece Flow

Batch and Push	Supermarket Pull	FIFO Lane	One-Piece Flow
Schedule each process and push to the next one	Upstream process replenishes what the downstream customer consumes	Fixed work-in-process between processes in first-in-first-out sequence	Linked processes without inventory in-between

1. Balance cycle times of equipment/assembly operations for the entire cell. (See **cellular layout**)

2. Set up U-shaped cell or straight line flow when constraints exist. (See **cellular layout**)

3. Cross-train all team members.

Cellular Layout

What is it?

The combination of equipment, material and people in close proximity to maximize flexibility, create flow and minimize non-value-added activities. Frequently, cellular layouts are in a "U" or "C" shape in order to allow cross-trained operators to move from one process to the other.

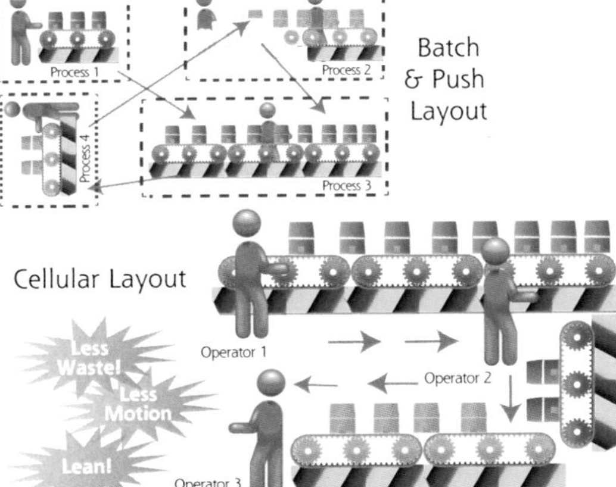

Why use it?

- Eliminates waste
- Creates capacity flexibility
- Allows for production flow to be seen. Contrary to a batch layout, people supporting a cell and building the product can see when a problem surfaces and can quickly act to maintain product flow to the customer.

Line Balancing

What is it?

The process of assigning tasks (workload) so every operator is doing the same amount of work in a "balanced" fashion to meet the customer's requirement or takt time.

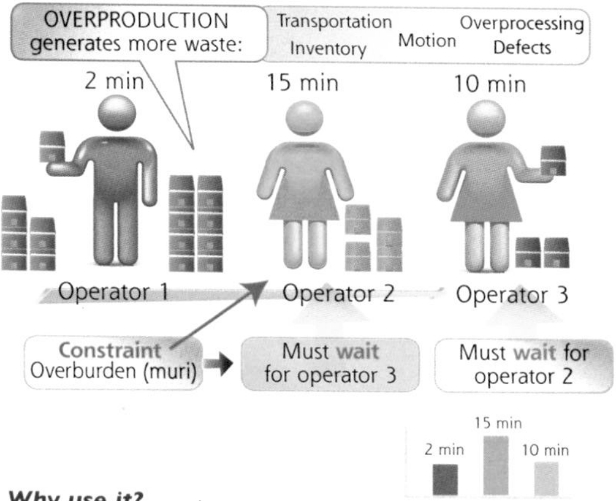

OVERPRODUCTION generates more waste:
Transportation
Inventory
Motion
Overprocessing
Defects

2 min
15 min
10 min

Operator 1
Operator 2
Operator 3

Constraint
Overburden (muri)
Must wait for operator 3
Must wait for operator 2

15 min
2 min
10 min

Why use it?

- Minimizes overburden
- Ensures that value flows from start to finish
- Reduces inventory by eliminating overproduction
- Optimizes the use of resources
- Reduces manufacturing lead time since everyone is providing the same amount of work and no one is waiting

Quick Changeover or SMED

What is it?

Quick Changeover or Single Minute Exchange of Dies (SMED) is a series of methods intended to reduce the time and effort for equipment changeover (setup) to an absolute minimum without adversely affecting quality.

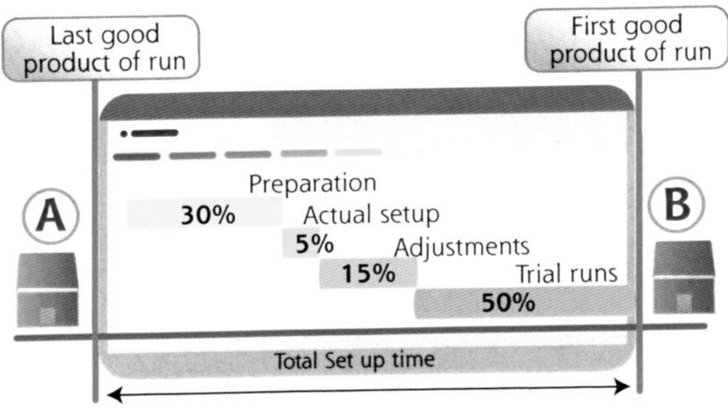

Why use it?

- Increases flexibility by enabling production of a greater variety of parts in smaller batches
- Ensures that the value flows from start to finish
- Reduces inventory by eliminating overproduction
- Optimizes the use of resources by minimizing machine downtime

How do I do it?

1. Document the setup and separate events into internal or external to identify opportunities for improvement

- **Internal Setup** is an activity that **must** be performed while the equipment is down
- **External Setup** is an activity that **could** be performed while the equipment is producing the parts

Quick Changeover Steps

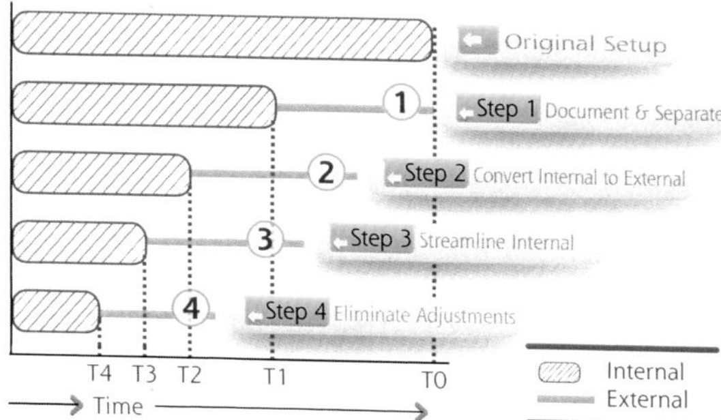

2. Convert internal events to external events
3. Streamline internal events by:
   - Simplifying Movement
   - Reducing Movement
   - Eliminating Movement
4. Eliminating adjustment trial runs by turning intuition and guessing into facts and settings
5. Continue improvement by repeating steps 2, 3 and 4

Total Productive Maintenance (TPM)

What is it?

A series of methods that ensures every piece of equipment in a production process always performs its required tasks so that production is never interrupted.

Why use it?

- Increases Overall Equipment Effectiveness (OEE): Availability, Performance and First Pass Yield (FPY) (Quality level)
- Reduces emergency downtime and need for "fire fighting" (work that must be done in response to an emergency)
- Increases employees' skill levels, knowledge and involvement

- Promotes cooperation and respect between the maintenance and production teams

How do I do it?

1. Perform initial machine cleaning
2. Identify and tag machine defects and leaks
3. Develop operator and preventative maintenance
4. Instruct operators in proper preventative maintenance techniques
5. Instruct maintenance staff in proper preventative maintenance techniques
6. Implement 5S around critical equipment
7. Monitor OEE and encourage cooperation

Overall Equipment Effectiveness

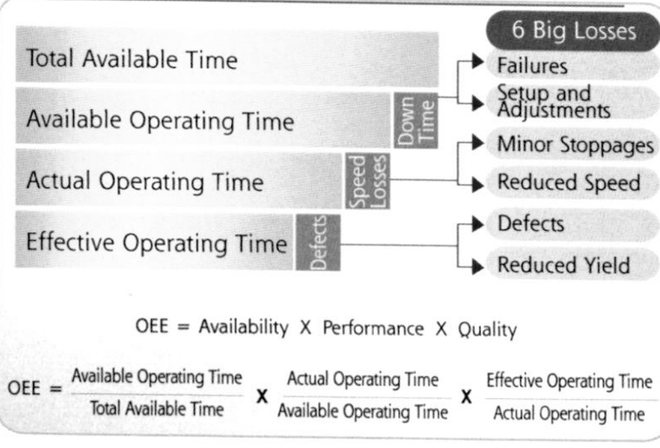

Get team members involved in maintaining their own equipment, and emphasize proactive and preventive maintenance.

Layered Process Audit (LPA)

What is it?

It is a set of audits focused on proactively identifying deviation from standards within critical processes as a way to prevent failures. The three elements of LPA are:

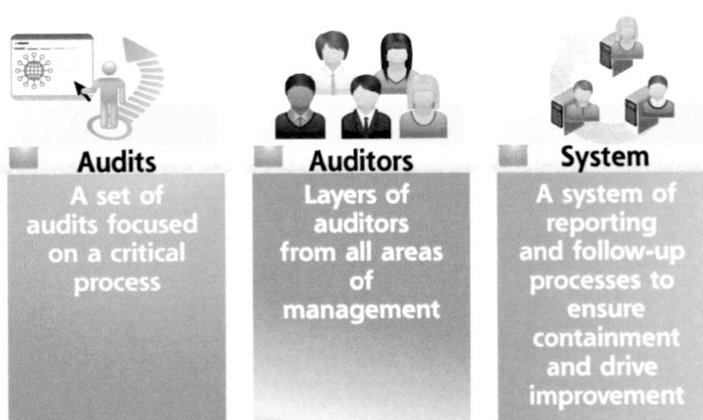

Audits
A set of audits focused on a critical process
Auditors
Layers of auditors from all areas of management
System
A system of reporting and follow-up processes to ensure containment and drive improvement

Why use it?

- Changes behavior from reacting to failures to preventing them
- Ensures critical processes are properly ready to work
- Provides opportunities for management to "go and see" as the first step for problem solving
- Makes opportunities for improvement visible and drives corrective and preventive actions

How do I do it?

1. Identify the critical processes and design the right questions (audits and checklist)
2. Perform shift, daily, weekly audits by all management layers, from top to bottom
3. Implement immediate containment and plan and follow-up improvement

Example of an LPA

Process: Shipping

LPA level: Manager

- Are supervisors following LPA procedures?
- Are LPA findings resolved as planned?
- Are work instructions followed? Observe two full cycles with supervisor for three operations
- Is the supervisor coaching on improving to meet the goal of one kaizen per person per month? Review the two most recent A3 reports
- Is the TPM procedure followed as planned? Review two procedures at each level

LPA level: Supervisor

- Are the operators starting their shifts on time?
- Are 5S procedures being followed?
- Is all of the equipment calibrated and is the calibration plan being followed?
- Are the operators following the training plan? Check multi-function matrix.

An LPA is critical to sustaining improved processes and in avoiding old habits.

Let Customers Pull

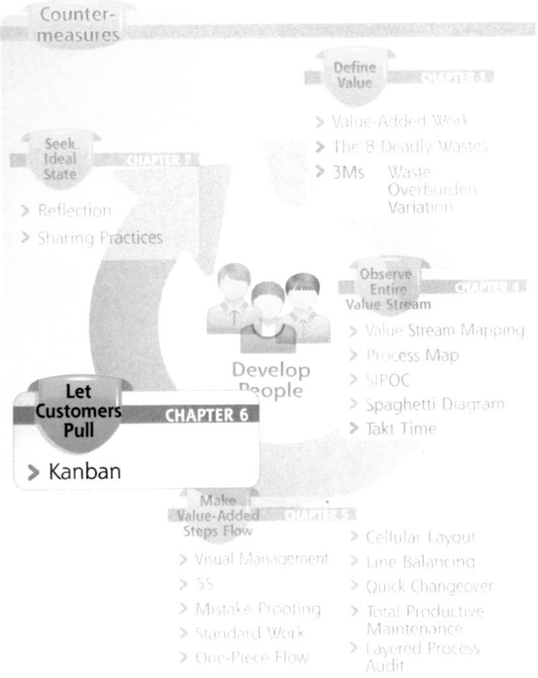

Counter-measures

Define Value CHAPTER 3
- Value-Added Work
- The 8 Deadly Wastes
- 3Ms Waste, Overburden, Variation

Seek Ideal State CHAPTER 7
- Reflection
- Sharing Practices

Develop People

Observe Entire Value Stream CHAPTER 4
- Value Stream Mapping
- Process Map
- SIPOC
- Spaghetti Diagram
- Takt Time

Let Customers Pull CHAPTER 6
- Kanban

Make Value-Added Steps Flow CHAPTER 5
- Visual Management
- 5S
- Mistake-Proofing
- Standard Work
- One-Piece Flow
- Cellular Layout
- Line Balancing
- Quick Changeover
- Total Productive Maintenance
- Layered Process Audit

Kanban System

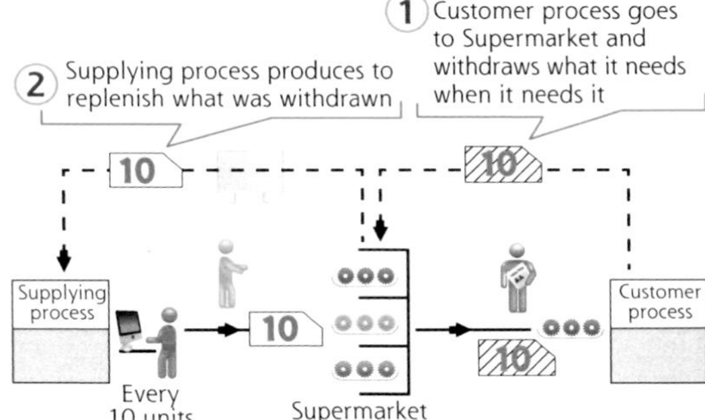

1 Customer process goes to Supermarket and withdraws what it needs when it needs it
2 Supplying process produces to replenish what was withdrawn
10
10
Supplying process
10
Every 10 units
Supermarket
10
Customer process

What is it?

A method of using visual signals **(kanban)** for triggering or controlling the **flow of materials** between processes internally or with outside suppliers.

Typical Kanban Card

Market and storage information	Product information	Process information
Market name and location, container type	Part name, number, description, quantity	Process name, location, machine or cell name

Why use it?

- Prevents overproduction as demand varies
- Provides specific production instructions of timing and quantity
- Serves as a quick visual control tool for production (Are you ahead or behind schedule?)
- Establishes a tool for continuous improvement (reduction of the number of kanban)

The Kanban "Talk"

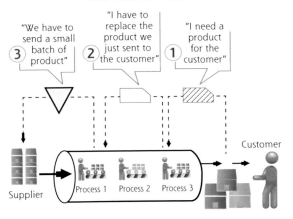

3 "We have to send a small batch of product"

2 "I have to replace the product we just sent to the customer"

1 "I need a product for the customer"

Supplier

Process 1

Process 2

Process 3

Customer

The Six Kanban Rules

Follow these six kanban rules:

1. Downstream processes always come to withdraw
2. Produce only the quantity withdrawn

3. Don't send defects to the next process
4. Kanban should be attached to the actual parts containers
5. For kanban to work, production must be leveled
6. The best kanban is not needing a kanban

How do I do it?

1. **Validate three conditions:**
   - Flow cannot be achieved between the two processes at this time. Remember rule number 6.
   - Equipment, process and people are reliable most of the time, at least 80% of the time.
   - Production has been leveled to avoid overcapacity and out of stock items.
2. Calculate the number of kanban cards (N):

   $$N = \left(\text{Average Demand} \times \text{Lead Time} + \text{Buffer} + \text{Safety Stock}\right) / \text{Container Size}$$

   Buffer = Inventory due to sudden fluctuations in customer orders

   Safety Stock = Inventory due to reliability issues in the process
3. Define the kanban cards and process for production and withdrawal. Train all participants by simulating the actual process
4. Implement and follow until kanban system is stable

Kanban systems are used only after a line has been stabled and balanced.

Chapter SEVEN

PURSUE PERFECTION

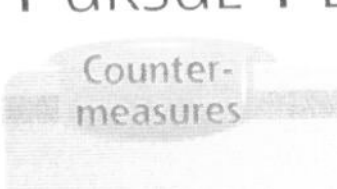

- Reflection
- Sharing Practices

Counter-measures

Define Value CHAPTER 3

- Value-Added Work
- The 8 Deadly Wastes
- 3Ms Waste Overburden Variation

Observe Entire Value Stream CHAPTER 4

- Value Stream Mapping
- Process Map
- SIPOC
- Spaghetti Diagram
- Takt Time

Develop People

Let Customers Pull CHAPTER 6

- Kanban

Make Value-Added Steps Flow CHAPTER 5

- Visual Management
- 5S
- Mistake-Proofing
- Standard Work
- One-Piece Flow
- Cellular Layout
- Line Balancing
- Quick Changeover
- Total Productive Maintenance
- Layered Process Audit

Reflection (hansei)

What is it?

The process of reflecting on ideas or experiences in order to learn from successes or failures to improve oneself in the future. It is a key step in kaizen, both for personal improvement and for process improvement in business.

Taiichi Ohno liked to say "Check is hansei." The "check" step of PDCA (Plan, Do, Check, Act) is an opportunity to reflect and learn before the Act/Adjust step in the PDCA cycle.

Why use it?

- Ensures you understand the causes of success or failure
- Avoids repeating the same mistakes in the future
- Reinforces our sense of humility so we don't stop learning and improving ourselves

How do I do it?

1. Confront the facts of your actions and behavior that resulted in success or failure
2. Use the 5 Whys technique to understand the reasoning and assumptions behind your actions
3. Question the validity of your assumptions
4. Define alternative assumptions, reasoning and/or actions in the context of the situation being reflected upon

THE SIX QUESTIONS WE SHOULD ASK

We should always ask six questions when moving toward our target condition (the challenge).

Plan

1. What is the target at this process?
2. What is the current condition?
3. What obstacles are preventing you from reaching the target?

Do

4. Which obstacles are you addressing?

Check

5. What is working? Are you getting the planned results?

Act

6. What did you learn about reaching the target?

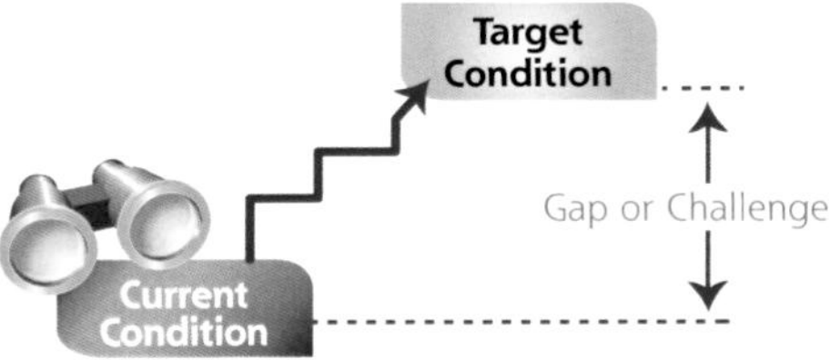

Better practices sharing (Yokoten)

What is it?

The process of horizontal learning of practices from one area to other areas as the final step of kaizen. Contrary to top-down approach, Yokoten focuses on peer-to-peer sharing as the final step of a kaizen project.

Successful Yokoten requires at least:

- Standard documentation of kaizen such as the A3 report
- Well defined processes to share better practices at all levels of the organization
- Leadership participation in sharing and reward sharing practices

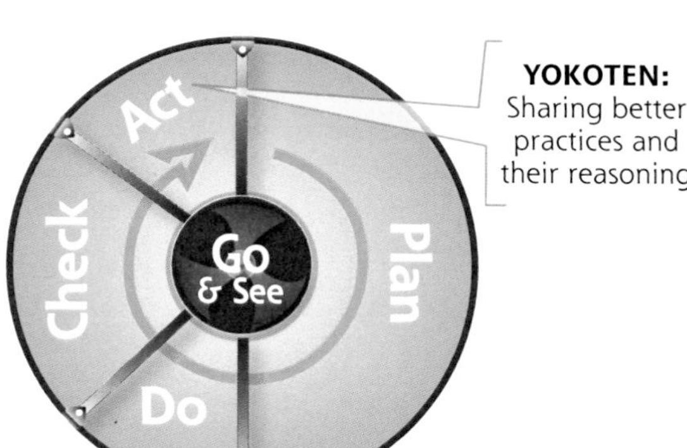

Why better practices instead of best practices? To avoid thinking that there are not more opportunities for improvement. The best practices are only temporary until a better practice is discovered. We can always improve.

Why use it?

- Multiplies proliferation of kaizen ideas (short-term results)
- Speeds improvement by implementing better practices
- Develops learning habits (long-term results)
- Teaches not only better practices but also the reasoning behind them

How do I do it?

- Use the standard forms such as the A3 report to document new practices as a result of a kaizen
- Validate metrics and requirements to confirm that it is in fact a better practice
- Define processes to share and implement better practices. Create incentives for replication
- Kaizen is not complete until yokoten is confirmed and the learning is shared with others

Yokoten is not only about copying a solution but mainly about the *thinking* behind the solution.

Glossary

A3 Report: A one-page document based on the Plan-Do-Check-Act Cycle. "A3" refers to an international size paper approximately 11x17 inches. Three common A3 reports are: Proposal, Status and Final.

3Fs Standard: The expectations for set FIXED location, FIXED item, FIXED quantity when completing the second step of 5S, Set in Order.

3Ms: Refer to the three targets that Lean Six Sigma focuses on eliminating: Waste (Muda), Overburden (Muri), and Variation (Mura).

5S or Sort, Set in Order, Shine, Standardize, Sustain: The 5-step methodology to create and maintain an organized workplace focusing on creating uninterrupted flow of material, people and information.

5 Whys: The method to ask "Why" several times to explore the cause/effect relationships underlying a particular problem.

8 Deadly Wastes: Any activity that does not add value from the customers' perspective and can be eliminated.

Batch Layout: Contrary to a cellular layout, batch layout allows a large number of similar products, called batch, to be held, processed and moved at once, making it difficult to reach one-piece flow.

Better Practices Sharing (Yokoten): The process of horizontal learning of practices from one area to other areas as the final step of kaizen. Contrary to top-down approach, Yokoten focuses on peer-to-peer sharing as the final step of a kaizen project.

Cellular Layout: The combination of equipment, material and people in close proximity to maximize flexibility, create flow and minimize non-value-added activities.

Countermeasures: The measures or actions taken to isolate and eliminate a problem. Countermeasures can be short or long term.

Current Value Stream Map: A map of how things currently operate.

Cycle of Improvement: The four steps are to standardize, expose problems, solve problems, and implement a new method.

Cycle Time: One of the three elements of standard work. The time required to complete an operation.

Defects: Any product or service that does not meet customer's specifications or steps to correct these defects (hidden factory).

DMAIC: The Define-Measure-Analyze-Improve-Control approach used to solve complex problems. DMAIC is a problem-solving methodology used in Six Sigma.

Door-to-door or Factory VSM: A type of value stream map used when only the steps within a factory or site are mapped, e.g., from receiving to shipping.

Extended or Enterprise VSM: A type of value stream map used when the entire value creation flow is mapped, including suppliers' and customers' material and information flow.

External Setup: The changeover or setup activities that could be performed while the equipment is producing parts.

Firefighting: The rushed activities performed in response to constant emergencies due to the lack of systematic problem solving.

Fishbone or Ishikawa Diagram: A visual description of the major possible causes of a particular problem.

Flow Chart: A visual and detailed description of the steps and their connections within a process.

Future Value Stream Map: The vision to becoming leaner in terms of creating flow by eliminating waste.

Hansei (Reflection): The process of reflecting on ideas or experiences in order to learn from successes or failures to improve oneself in the future. It is a key step in kaizen, both for personal improvement and for process improvement.

Higher Why: An extension of the 5 Whys to evaluate new potential solutions when the perceived problem is too narrow.

Internal Setup: The changeover or setup activities that must be performed while the equipment is down.

Inventory: Material or work on hand other than what's needed right now to satisfy customer demand.

IPO (Input-Process-Output): The visual representation used to provide a big picture understanding of the process. Usually used for project scoping purposes. Also see SIPOC.

Ishikawa Diagram: See Fishbone Diagram.

Kanban System: A method of using visual signals (kanban) for triggering or controlling the flow of materials between processes internally or with outside suppliers. They are used only after a line has been stabilized and balanced.

Kaizen Events: A temporary, intensive, time compressed and disruptive effort driven by a group of people with the objective to implement several changes at the same time.

Layered Process Audit (LPA): A set of audits focused on proactively identifying deviation from standards within critical processes as a way to prevent failures.

Lead Time: The actual time to produce a unit from start to end, including non-value-added activities and waste, e.g., rework, delays, transportation.

Lean Index Assessment: A tool to evaluate cultural and technical elements of Lean Six Sigma maturity allowing teams to identify gaps and drive action plans to reach higher levels of lean maturity.

Line Balancing: The process of assigning tasks (workload) so every operator is doing the same amount of work in a "balanced" fashion to meet the customer's requirement.

Material and Information Flow Diagram: See Value Stream Map.

Mistake Proofing: Simple devices intended to achieve mistake-free processes by preventing errors from occurring in the first place, or detecting errors in the process as early as possible.

Model Line: A strategy to enable rapid development and replication of Lean Six Sigma deployment by using an area or production line as model or pilot within the organization.

Muda: Any wasteful activity as described in the 8 Deadly Wastes. It is part of the 3Ms.

Mura or Variation: The irregular flow of work, material or information. It can be seen as a source of Muri (Overburden) and Muda (wasteful activity). It is part of the 3Ms.

Muri or Overburden: When a person or machine is pushed beyond natural limits. It is part of the 3Ms.

Overall Equipment Effectiveness (OEE): A metric to measure equipment effectiveness at three levels: availability, performance and quality.

One-Piece Flow: The ideal state of efficient operations, where batch sizes are replaced by working on one unit at a time and passing each piece to the next process without delay and only when it is requested.

Pareto Chart: A chart that displays occurrences from the most frequent to the least frequent, usually expressed as a count or percentage. Used to identify the most significant contributors to a problem.

Pareto Principle: "80% of the problems come from 20% of the causes."

Plan-Do-Check-Act (PDCA): A practical sequence of steps for solving problems.

Poka-yoke: See Mistake Proofing.

Process Map: Any diagram that describes the material, people or information flow, or a combination of them, in the creation of a product or service. Process maps can be used to represent current or expected conditions of a process.

Quick Changeover: A series of methods intended to reduce the time and effort for equipment changeover (setup) to an absolute minimum without adversely affecting quality.

Red Tag: A red label used to identify potential unneeded items when doing the sort step during 5S.

Red Flag Conditions: Potential sources of errors in a process.

Set in Order: The second step of 5S. Organize the workplace to make the flow of materials, people, and information visually evident to all.

Shine: The third step of 5S. Clean to eliminate sources.

Single Minute Exchange of Dies (SMED): See Quick Changeover.

SIPOC: A high-level chart that describes the five components of any value creation chain: Supplier, Input, Process, Output and Customer. Usually used for project scoping purposes.

Sort: The first step of 5S. Keep what is needed and remove everything else.

SOP: Standard Operating Procedure. The document detailing steps of a process.

Standardize: The fourth step of 5S. Define who, when and how often you should do the first 3Ss. (Sort, Set in order, Shine)

Standard Work: The description of actions performed by people and machines carrying out value added work in an efficient way, in the right sequence and time, using the right tools. The three most common documents used for standard work are: standard work sheet, standard work combination table, and operator or work instruction.

Spaghetti Diagram: A chart of the material and/or people flow through the physical layout required to create a product or service.

Sponsor: Person(s) who can make decisions, arbitrate solutions and prioritize resources.

Sustain: The fifth step of the 5S. Periodic evaluation of the 5S system (audits) and celebration of successes.

Swim-lane Chart: A chart used to identify interaction of the departments or people involved in the process.

TIM WOODS: The mnemonic used to remember the 8 Deadly Wastes: Transportation, Inventory, Motion, Waiting, Overproduction, Over-processing, Defects, Skills Unused.

Takt Time: The time needed to produce one quality part to meet customer demand.

Total Productive Maintenance (TPM): A series of methods that ensures every piece of equipment in a production process is always able to perform its required tasks so that production is never interrupted. It is a team-based and continuous activity that enhances normal equipment maintenance activities and involves every worker.

Value Stream: A sequence of activities, value added, non-value added and waste, required to produce a product or service.

Value Stream Map (VSM): A graphic representation of current or future material and information flow from beginning to end. There are three types: extended or enterprise, door-to-door or factory, and process.

Variation: See Mura.

Visual Management: Simple controls aimed to make normal and abnormal conditions visible so standards can easily be followed by all employees and to make waste visible so it can be eliminated and prevented.

Waiting: The idle time when people, materials, information or equipment is not available when required.

Waste: See Muda.

Work-In-Process (WIP): The processed material or information that has not been fully completed to become final product or service.

Yokoten: See Better Practices Sharing (Yokoten).

INDEX

P

Q

R

S

T

V

W

Y

QUIZ
ANSWER KEY

1. D
2. A
3. A
4. A
5. A
6. D
7. B
8. C
9. D
10. C
11. A
12. C
13. A
14. A